Electronic Projects in Audio

Other Constructors Projects Books

Electronic Projects in Audio

R. A. Penfold
Series Editor Philip Chapman

Newnes Technical Books

The Butterworth Group

United Kingdom   **Butterworth & Co (Publishers) Ltd**
London: 88 Kingsway, WC2B 6AB

Australia   **Butterworths Pty Ltd**
Sydney: 586 Pacific Highway, Chatswood, NSW 2067
Also at Melbourne, Brisbane, Adelaide and Perth

Canada   **Butterworth & Co (Canada) Ltd**
Toronto: 2265 Midland Avenue, Scarborough,
Ontario M1P 4S1

New Zealand   **Butterworths of New Zealand Ltd**
Wellington: T & W Young Building
77—85 Customhouse Quay, 1, CPO Box 472

South Africa   **Butterworth & Co (South Africa) (Pty) Ltd**
Durban: 152—154 Gale Street

USA   **Butterworth (Publishers) Inc**
Boston: 19 Cummings Park, Woburn, Mass. 01801

First published 1979

© Butterworth & Co (Publishers) Ltd, 1979

British Library Cataloguing in Publication Data

Penfold, R A
    Electronic projects in audio.
    1. Sound — Recording and reproducing —
    Amateurs' manuals
    I. Title
    621.389′33   TK9968   78-40660

ISBN 0-408-00338-3

Typeset by Butterworths Litho Preparation Department
Printed in England by William Clowes & Sons Ltd
Beccles and London

Preface

To most people the word *audio* probably conjures up mental images of sophisticated hi-fi equipment such as tuners, amplifiers, cassette decks and the like. Such equipment really falls outside the scope of this book which is intended as a source of relatively simple but useful designs for the home constructor of limited experience. However, many of the designs can be used in conjunction with sophisticated hi-fi gear to increase its performance and versatility. There is usually a significant saving in cost by building one's own electronic equipment and ancillary gear, but perhaps more important than this, there are many types of home constructor circuit which are not produced commercially, and this gives the amateur electronics enthusiast an opportunity to make improvements which would not otherwise be possible.

Of course, there are other areas of audio apart from hi-fi, and there are circuits here which will find use in the spheres of amateur tape recording, electronic music and others.

Some of the circuits are extremely simple; using just one active device and a few passive components, but some of the others are rather more complex. They are all useful and practical designs which should not be beyond the capabilities of most beginners as details of electrical construction and notes on mechanical construction are provided for each circuit.

Contents

1

Rumble Filter

Probably the main limiting factors on the reproduction quality of most record player systems are the noise produced by the record deck, and noise actually present on the record itself. The noise produced by any record deck is virtually all at very low frequencies and is usually termed 'rumble'. Usually this noise is almost entirely at frequencies which are below the lower limit of human hearing. However, a significant amount of rumble within the audio frequency spectrum is produced by some decks, and even very low frequency rumble can produce audible signals due to intermodulation distortion.

Rumble is sometimes present to a significant degree on records, particularly on old or inexpensive recordings. Records can develop slight warps even if they are carefully and correctly stored, and these warps can cause quite large very low frequency signals to be produced. This form of rumble can be particularly noticeable and annoying.

The circuit

A rumble filter is a device which greatly reduces rumble by rapidly rolling off the low frequency response of the amplifier used in a record playing system. The circuit diagram of such a filter is shown in Fig. 1.1.

TR1 is used in the emitter follower configuration, and therefore has only unity voltage gain. It is biased by R2 and R3, and R4 is its emitter load resistor.

A simple CR bass cut filter is formed by the series capacitance of C1 and C2 feeding into the combined parallel impedance of R2, R3 and the input impedance of TR1. This operates by virtue of the fact that the impedance of a capacitor rises with decreasing frequency. Thus at middle and high frequencies the impedance through C1 and C2 is low in comparison with the impedance into which they are working. At low

1

frequencies their impedance rises, causing significant losses through the circuit.

A single section CR filter of this type produces only a rather gradual initial roll off rate, and the ultimate roll off rate is only 6dB per octave (i.e. halving the input frequency causes a 50% reduction in circuit gain).

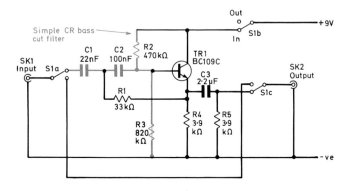

Figure 1.1

Rumble filter circuit. R1 is the 'bootstrapping' resistor

Ideally a filter of this type should have a well defined initial roll off frequency and an ultimate attenuation rate of 12dB per octave (i.e. halving the input frequency causing a 75% reduction in circuit gain).

The necessary improvement in performance is provided by R1 which is what is known as a 'bootstrapping' resistor. At middle and high frequencies this component has no significant effect on the circuit as it appears to have an infinite impedance to the input signal. This happens because TR1 has unity voltage gain, and so any variation in the potential at the left hand end of R1 is matched by an almost identical change at the other end. Thus no input current can flow through R1 as no voltage is developed across it, and it has an apparent infinite impedance.

At low frequencies there is not unity voltage gain between the junction of R1 – C1 – C2 and TR1 emitter as the CR filter introduces significant losses. This decreases the effective impedance of R1 at low frequencies, and it forms a second CR filter in conjunction with C1. This produces a much better defined cut off frequency, and increases the attenuation rate to about 12dB per octave.

One problem with this type of circuit is that it produces a slight peak in the frequency response just above the cut-off frequency. In this case the peak is at a frequency of about 50Hz, which is a little unfortunate as many record decks produce a certain amount of rumble at this frequency. A CR high pass filter has therefore been added at the output in order to round off this slight peak. This additional filtering also slightly speeds up the roll off rate of the circuit. The filter is formed by C3 and R5.

The graph which appears in Fig. 1.2 shows the frequency response of the prototype filter. The cut off frequency is 50Hz and the ultimate attenuation rate is approximately 15dB per octave. Noise and distortion produced by the circuit are negligible as TR1 is used with 100% negative feedback.

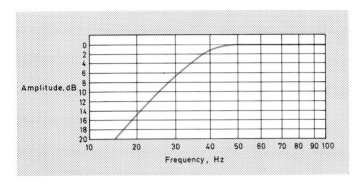

Figure 1.2

Frequency response of the prototype rumble filter

S1 provides both in/out and on/off switching. S1b acts as an ordinary on/off switch while S1a and S1c simply bypass the filter in the 'out' position.

Construction

With the only exception of S1, all the components are mounted on a 0.1in matrix stripboard which has 14 holes by 15 copper strips. The component layout of this panel is illustrated in Fig. 1.3, which also shows the other wiring of the unit.

When a board of the appropriate size has been cut out it is advisable to file flat any rough edges to produce a neat finish. The six breaks in the copper strips can then be made, either using the special spot face cutting tool or a small twist drill (about 4mm diameter) held in the hand. The two mounting holes are then drilled. These can be 3.2mm ($\frac{1}{10}$ in) diameter, and they will then accept either 6B.A. or M3 mounting bolts. The various components can then be soldered into position.

Care must be taken when wiring up S1 as suitable rotary switches are produced by several manufacturers, and each manufacturer seems to use a different contact arrangement. If the contact arrangement is not marked on the switch it is advisable to check this using a continuity tester.

3

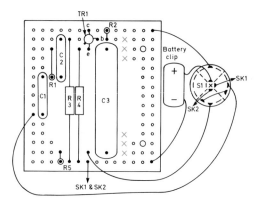

Figure 1.3

Component layout and wiring of the rumble filter.
(See appendix for transistor lead identification)
X indicates a break in the copper strip

It is recommended that the project should be housed in a metal case so that the circuit is screened from electrical interference. The unit is described here in mono form, but if a stereo filter is required it is merely necessary to build two units, one for each channel. A single switch could then be used to control both channels, and this would need to have five poles. Suitable rotary switches are available but are rather expensive, and a push button switch would probably be a more practical alternative.

4

The unit is designed to be used between the preamplifier and power amplifier stages of the amplifier. Many amplifiers have either a pre-amplifier output/main amplifier input or tape monitor facility, either of which will provide a suitable insertion point for the filter.

The circuit has quite a high input impedance, and so if the record deck is fitted with a crystal or ceramic cartridge it is perfectly accept-able to connect the filter between the record deck and the amplifier.

It is also possible to do this if the record deck is fitted with a magnetic cartridge, but results may not be entirely satisfactory. The output from a magnetic cartridge is considerably less than that produced by a crystal or ceramic pick-up, and so the noise generated by the filter will receive a considerable amount of amplification. This may well result in a

Table 1.1. Components list for rumble filter

Resistors (all miniature ¼W, 5%)
R1	33kΩ
R2	470kΩ
R3	820kΩ
R4	3.9kΩ
R5	3.9kΩ

Capacitors
C1	22nF type C280
C2	100nF type C280
C3	2.2µF type C280

Semiconductor
TR1	BC109C

Switch
S1	3-pole 2-way rotary type (e.g. three poles of a 3-way 4-pole switch with adjustable end stop set for 2 way operation, see text).

Miscellaneous
metal case
0.1in matrix stripboard panel
PP3 battery and connector to suit
input and output sockets
connecting wire, control knob, solder, etc.
Note that two sets of components are required for stereo operation.

noticeable reduction in the signal to noise ratio of the system, although results should still be more than adequate in this respect. The input impedance of the circuit is far too high to properly match a magnetic cartridge, which usually requires a load impedance of about 47kΩ.

Therefore a resistor of 56kΩ in value should be added across the input of the filter if it is to be used in this way, in order to reduce the input impedance to about the correct level.

Regardless of how the filter is fitted into the audio system, screened leads must be used at both the input and output of the unit.

The best cut off frequency for equipment of this type depends to some extent on the equipment with which it is used. When used with the more expensive types of record deck it would probably be better to have a lower cut off frequency as there will otherwise be an unnecessary attenuation of the lower audio frequencies. On the other hand, a higher cut off frequency will probably produce significantly reduced rumble if the unit is used with an inexpensive and relatively unsophisticated record deck. The cut off frequency is easily changed, and it is merely necessary to alter the values of the three capacitors. The cut off frequency is inversely proportional to the values of these components (i.e. doubling their values halves the cut off frequency, and halving their values doubles the cut off frequency).

2

Scratch Filter

Although there are several types of efficient record cleaning device available these days, not everyone bothers to use them, and they do not necessarily prevent records from becoming spoilt by a gradual accumulation of minute dust particles in the grooves, and the small scratches which this dust can cause. This can result in the enjoyment obtained from records being impaired by the familiar constant crackle caused by small scratches and particles of dust.

Fortunately the signals produced in this way consist to a large extent of very high audio frequencies, with the main content being at frequencies above about 6 or 7kHz. Thus it is possible to greatly attenuate this noise by rapidly rolling off the frequency response of the amplifier above about 6 to 7kHz, and this is precisely what a scratch filter does.

It must be stressed here that a simple filter of this kind cannot deal effectively with deep scratches which usually produce a significant output at middle and even bass frequencies in a severe case. This filter is only intended to counteract the effects of small scratches and dust particles, or surface noise as it is often termed.

The circuit

The circuit diagram of the scratch filter appears in Fig. 2.1, and this is in many ways similar to the rumble filter described in the previous section of this book.

TR1 is used in the common collector mode and is biased by R1 and R2 via R3 and R4. R5 and R6 form the emitter load resistance for TR1. C1 provides d.c. blocking at the input, and C4 provides the same function at the output.

An RC treble cut filter is formed by the series resistance of R3 and R4 feeding the shunt capacitor C3. At middle and low audio frequencies the impedance of C3 is too high to have any significant effect on the circuit, but at high frequencies its impedance becomes low in comparison to the series impedance of R3 and R4. This results in large losses being produced through R3 and R4.

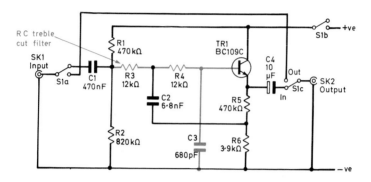

Figure 2.1

Circuit of the scratch filter

As was the case with the previous circuit, this produces a roll off rate of 6dB per octave, except that this time the circuit gain *falls* with increasing input frequency, of course. A roll off rate of about 12dB per octave is more desirable, and so bootstrapping is again used to improve the performance of the circuit. This time the bootstrapping is provided by a capacitor (C2), and at low and middle audio frequencies this appears to possess an infinite impedance. At high frequencies where the gain of the circuit falls below unity C2 has a significant impedance, and forms a second RC treble cut filter in conjection with R3. This produces a better defined cut off frequency and increases the attenuation rate to about 12dB per octave.

At first sight it might seem unnecessary to use a split emitter resistance for TR1 with C2 being fed from the junction of the two resistors. Indeed, it would be reasonable to expect this to have an adverse effect on performance with a slightly reduced attenuation rate being produced. This does in fact cause some loss of performance, but it is necessary in order to prevent an excessive peak being produced in the frequency response just below the cut off frequency. By reducing the gain in the bootstrapping circuit in this way, the peak in the response is reduced to an insignificant level and the attenuation rate of the circuit is only fractionally less than 12dB per octave.

The frequency response of the prototype scratch filter is shown in Fig. 2.2. There is a peak in the response at about 3.5kHz, but as this is only about + 1dB with only a gradual roll off either side, it is of no real

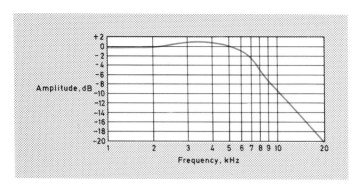

Figure 2.2

Frequency response of the scratch filter

consequence and does not produce any audible results. There is a 2dB roll off from 5.5 to 7kHz before the ultimate roll off rate is reached.

Incidentally, the scratch and rumble filters described here use a well known configuration which is often employed in audio equipment, and is known as the Sallen and Key arrangement.

Construction

The scratch filter is assembled on a piece of stripboard as shown in Fig. 2.3. The panel has 13 by 15 holes with the copper strips running across the width of the board. When a board of the correct size has been cut out, the six breaks in the copper strips and the two 3.2mm diameter mounting holes are drilled before the components are soldered into position.

The remaining wiring can then be completed, and this is all illustrated in Fig. 2.3. As with the previous circuit, for stereo operation two circuits must be constructed, one being inserted into each channel. If this is done S1 can conveniently be a multipole pushbutton switch which is used to control both channels.

It is recommended that the unit is housed in a metal case so that the circuit is screened. Of course, the component panel(s) must be spaced off the case slightly in order to avoid short circuits, and care must be taken to ensure that none of the wiring accidentally short circuits to the case.

Using the scratch filter

All the points on the use of the rumble filter also apply to the scratch filter (except the last paragraph on p.6), so they will not be repeated here.

If the constructor wishes to incorporate both the scratch and rumble filters into an audio system it is quite feasible to do so. It is merely necessary to connect the filters in series, the order is of no consequence.

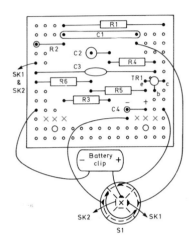

Figure 2.3

Layout and wiring details. × indicates a break in the copper strip

Although these filters have been described here as self contained add-on units, they can be built into a home-constructed amplifier if desired. The 9V battery supply could then be replaced by the supply rail of the main equipment, provided this is between 6 and 20V, and is reasonably well smoothed and decoupled. The current consumption of each of these circuits is typically a little in excess of 1mA from a 9V supply.

Table 2.1. Components list for scratch filter

Resistors (all miniature, ¼W, 5%)
R1	470kΩ
R2	820kΩ
R3	12kΩ
R4	12kΩ
R5	470Ω
R6	3.9kΩ

Capacitors
C1	470nF type C280
C2	6.8nF polystyrene
C3	680pF ceramic plate
C4	10μF, 10V

Semiconductor
TR1	BC109C

Switch
S1	3 pole, 2 way rotary type (e.g. three poles of a 3 way 4 pole switch with adjustable end stop set for two way operation).

Miscellaneous
metal case
0.1in matrix stripboard panel
PP3 battery and connector to suit
input and output sockets
connecting wire, control knob, solder, etc.
Note that two sets of components are required for stereo operation.

3

Dynamic Microphone Preamplifier

Low impedance moving coil (dynamic) microphones offer a reasonable level of performance, ruggedness, and low cost, and are therefore extremely popular. Microphones of this type have only an extremely low output signal level though, and are unsuitable for direct connection to many pieces of audio equipment. If you wish to use one with a hi-fi amplifier, for instance, inputs such as *Aux.* or *Tape* will be something in the region of 1000 times too insensitive and are obviously totally useless in this application. A *Mag.* input will not be much better as it will still be something in the region of 10 to 20 times too insensitive, and inputs of this type are RIAA equalised anyway (the input signal is subjected to considerable bass boost and treble cut).

It is also possible to run into difficulties with this type of microphone when a long microphone lead is used. As the signal levels in this lead are only extremely small, only a very small pick up of mains hum is needed in order to produce a significant nuisance. This can be overcome by using a preamplifier close to the microphone so that a comparatively high level signal is fed down the long lead. A very small pick up of mains hum is then insignificant when the wanted signal in the lead is at a level of (say) a few hundred millivolts r.m.s.

The preamplifier described here can be used to boost the output from a low impedance moving coil microphone to a level of about 500mV r.m.s. This is sufficient to drive any amplifier, mixer, tape recorder, etc., which does not already have a suitable microphone input. The unit requires an input level of only about 200µV in order to produce an output amplitude of 500mV. The unweighted signal to noise ratio of the unit is approximately -66dB (input left open circuit). The input impedance of the amplifier is about 600Ω which provides a good match to most low impedance dynamic microphones, including many high quality types. Electret microphones having an integral high to low impedance matching preamplifier can also be used with this unit. It is not suitable for use with high impedance (50kΩ) dynamic microphones or with crystal types.

The circuit

Fig. 3.1 shows the complete circuit diagram of the low impedance dynamic microphone preamplifier. This type of preamplifier often obtains the necessary low input impedance by using a resistor to shunt the input of an amplifier having a relatively high input impedance.

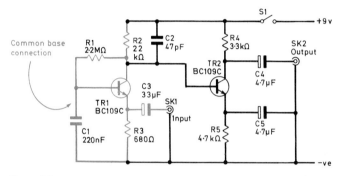

Figure 3.1

Circuit diagram of the 600Ω dynamic mic preamp. TR1 is connected in common base to give a low input impedance

The alternative to this is to use a common base input stage, as a transistor amplifier of this type has an inherently low input impedance. The latter is the method used here.

TR1 is used as the basis of the input stage, and it is biased by R1. R2 is its collector load resistor and C1 couples its base to earth. R3 is the emitter resistor, and this sets the input impedance of the amplifier at approximately the required level of 600Ω. C3 provides d.c. blocking at the input.

In order to obtain a fairly low noise level, a high-gain low-noise transistor is used in the TR1 position, and it is run at a collector current of only about 200µA or so. This stage provides a reasonable voltage gain, but the signal level at TR1 collector is still quite small and requires considerable further amplification.

TR2 provides most of the gain, and this is connected as a high-gain common-emitter amplifier. Its base is direct coupled to the

13

collector of TR1 which provides the base bias voltage for TR2. TR1 is biased so that about 4V appears at its collector, and R1 is connected between the base and collector of TR1 so that this biasing is stabilised by a certain amount of negative feedback. The potential at TR2 emitter will be about 0.5V or so lower than the base voltage, or about 3.5V in other words. The emitter and collector currents of a high gain transistor are virtually identical, and so obviously the voltage developed across R4 will be about 30% lower than that developed across R5, as the value of R4 is about 30% lower than that of R5. This means that very roughly 2.5V is developed across R4, which with a 9V supply leaves about 3V between the emitter and collector terminals of TR2.

This form of biasing is very reliable, and it is not necessary to alter resistor values to suit the particular transistors employed in the circuit. The unit is capable of an output level of about 5V peak to peak without clipping occurring, and this gives an adequate overload margin.

The emitter of TR1 must be decoupled to earth as the a.c. negative feedback introduced by R5 would otherwise reduce its voltage gain to less than unity. C5 provides this decoupling. Of course, R5 still introduces a large amount of d.c. negative feedback which stabilises the biasing of the circuit. Output d.c. blocking is provided by C4. C2 rolls off the high frequency response of the amplifier which would otherwise extend well above the audio frequency spectrum, making the unit sensitive to stray pick up of strong radio signals. S1 is an ordinary on/off switch.

Construction

A suitable 0.1in matrix stripboard layout for the preamplifier is illustrated in Fig. 3.2. The component panel has 10 by 16 holes with the copper strips running across the width of the board. There are no breaks in any of the copper strips.

This component layout is fairly compact and care must be taken to ensure that none of the component leadout wires accidentally short together. Also, the gap between the strips of 0.1in matrix stripboard is necessarily very small, and it is very easy to accidentally bridge two adjacent strips with a blob of excess solder, especially when a very compact component layout is being used. If the completed project fails to work for no apparent reason it is a good idea to check for short circuits between strips using a continuity tester. Short circuits of this type are notoriously difficult to spot with the naked eye.

The circuit is extremely sensitive and it is virtually essential to enclose the unit in a metal case in order to screen it from mains hum and similar sources of electrical interference. The case should be connected to the negative supply rail, and this will normally be accomplished via the input sockets anyway. These sockets were 3.5mm jack types on the prototype, but phono, DIN, standard jack types, etc. can be used if preferred. It is not necessary to use screened input and output cables within the metal case, but the external connecting cables must be screened (the outer braiding of these leads connects to the case and the negative supply rail of the preamplifier).

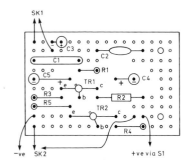

Figure 3.2

Component layout on the matrix board

Although the circuit has a very high voltage gain it is very stable as the input impedance is quite low, and the input and output of the circuit are in anti-phase. Any stray feedback will therefore be of the negative variety.

The current consumption of the unit is typically slightly less than 1mA from a 9V supply, and so even with extensive use the PP3 battery will have virtually its shelf life.

15

Table 3.1. Components list for dynamic microphone preamplifier

Resistors (all miniature, 5 or 10% tolerance)
R1   2.2MΩ
R2   22kΩ
R3   680Ω
R4   3.3kΩ
R5   4.7kΩ

Capacitors
C1   220nF type C280
C2   47pF ceramic plate
C3   33μF, 6V
C4   4.7μF, 10V
C5   4.7μF, 10V

Semiconductors
TR1   BC109C
TR2   BC109C

Switch
S1   S.P.S.T. toggle or miniature toggle type

Miscellaneous
metal case
0.1in matrix stripboard panel
PP3 battery and connector to suit
input and output sockets
wire, solder, etc.

4

Magnetic Cartridge Preamplifier

It is commonplace for a crystal or ceramic pickup to be used in budget record playing equipment. In general these types of cartridge are less expensive than the magnetic type, and they also require less sophisticated amplifying equipment. However, in many respects a crystal or ceramic cartridge offers a level of performance which is noticeably inferior to a magnetic pick-up.

A reasonably good quality magnetic pick-up is not exorbitantly expensive, and the reproduction quality of an inexpensive record playing system can usually be improved to a worthwhile extent by changing a crystal or ceramic pickup for a magnetic one. Unfortunately this is not always a straightforward job.

Assuming there are no problems with mechanical compatibility (the cartridge must fit the arm!), there may still be electrical incompatibility if the amplifying equipment does not have an input for a magnetic cartridge. An input which is designed to accept the output from a crystal or ceramic pickup is totally unsuitable for direct connection to a magnetic cartridge.

This is partly due to the fact that the output from a magnetic cartridge is fairly low, and is usually something in the region of 5mV r.m.s. The output from a ceramic cartridge is usually about 100 times greater than this. A great deal of additional gain is therefore required. Another problem is that a magnetic pickup is usually designed to operate into an impedance of 47kΩ, whereas a crystal or ceramic input usually has an input impedance of about 1MΩ.

It is not just a matter of providing extra gain and the correct input impedance either, as the output from a magnetic pickup has to be equalised in order to obtain a flat frequency response. All modern records are produced using what is called the 'constant velocity' system. With this system the pickup must produce an output signal which is proportional to the speed at which the stylus moves in order to produce a flat frequency response. Magnetic cartridges are compatible with this system. However, equalisation is still necessary as a considerable amount of treble boost is applied to the signal which is recorded onto the disc. In conjunction with the treble cut which is applied at the playing system this produces a flat frequency response and a greatly improved signal to noise ratio. Apart from this treble boost the recorded signal is given a large amount of bass cut, as without this there would be excessively large groove modulations on high level bass signals, and this could result in groove wall collapse. The record playing equipment must therefore apply the correct amount of bass boost to the signal in order to correct the frequency response.

Paradoxically, crystal and ceramic cartridges are not compatible with the constant velocity recording system, but are compatible with the constant amplitude system. The constant velocity system with bass cut and treble boost produces a good approximation of the constant amplitude system, and so crystal and ceramic cartridges give fairly good results without any equalisation.

The circuit

Fig. 4.1 shows the circuit diagram of a simple preamplifier which will match a magnetic cartridge to a crystal or ceramic input, or any other

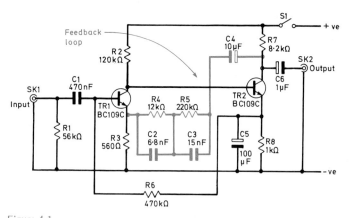

Figure 4.1

The circuit schematic of the magnetic cartridge preamp. The feedback loop providing the equalisation is shown in colour

high level unequalised input for that matter. At middle frequencies it has a gain of about 40 times, but this can be increased if necessary. The overload margin is in excess of 20dB (10 times) when an 18V supply is used.

The circuit uses a conventional two-transistor direct-coupled arrangement. Both transistors are used in the common emitter configuration, but a considerable amount of a.c. and d.c. negative feedback is used. Base biasing for TR1 is provided from TR2 emitter via R6. This biasing system is very reliable as it is stabilised by a considerable amount of feedback. R2 is the collector load resistor for TR1, and this is given a very high value so that TR1 operates at a very low collector current (about 100μA) and provides a low noise level.

A.C. negative feedback is provided between TR2 collector and TR1 emitter, and it is here that the equalisation is applied. The equalisation components are R4, R5, C2 and C3, with C4 being used to provide d.c. blocking. The equalisation operates on the principle that the impedance of a capacitor falls with increasing signal frequency. At middle frequencies the value of C3 is such that it introduces a large amount of negative feedback to the circuit, with a consequent reduction in gain. With decreasing frequency its impedance rises significantly and the gain of the overall circuit is boosted by the decrease in feedback. At middle frequencies C2 has an impedance which is high in relation to R4 and it therefore has very little effect on the level of feedback. At high frequencies its impedance becomes low in comparison to R4, and this results in increased feedback and decreased gain. In this way the required shaping of the frequency response is accomplished.

The basic input impedance of the circuit is quite high, and R1 is used to shunt the input impedance to give approximately the required level of 47kΩ. This system has the advantage of enabling a fairly small input d.c. blocking capacitor to be used (C1). This ensures that only a very small and insignificant current flows through the cartridge at switch on and switch off as this capacitor charges and discharges respectively.

Output d.c. blocking is provided by C6. S1 is the ordinary *on/off* switch. The current consumption of the amplifier is only about 1mA from an 18V supply.

Construction

The recommended component layout for the unit is shown in Fig. 4.2. This is based on a 0.1in matrix stripboard which has 25 holes by 15 copper strips. Remember to drill the two mounting holes and make the four breaks in the copper strips before soldering the components into position. It is advisable to use screened leads at the input and output, and the unit should be mounted in a metal case to provide overall screening. Solder pins should be inserted into the panel at the points where the outer braiding of the input and output leads will connect to the board. This is necessary as the outer braiding will be too thick to fit into the holes in the board. Both the pins and the braiding should be generously tinned with solder prior to making these connections, and a good strong joint should then be produced.

The circuit is described here in mono form, but for stereo, two of these devices will be needed, one for each channel.

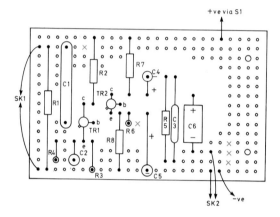

Figure 4.2

Component layout (X indicates a break in the copper strip)

Make sure that the metal case is earthed to the negative supply rail. Normally this connection will be made via the input and output sockets. These were phono types on the prototype preamplifier, but other types can be used if preferred.

Using the preamplifier

In order to ensure a good overload margin it is necessary to power the unit from an 18V supply. This can conveniently be supplied by a couple

20

of PP3 batteries connected in series. As the current consumption is only about 1mA per channel these batteries will have virtually their shelf life with normal usage. The unit will work with a 9V supply, and results may well be satisfactory using a single PP3 provided the pickup doesn't have a high output.

A few magnetic cartridges are designed to operate into an impedance of 100kΩ and not 47kΩ. The preamplifier can be modified for an input impedance of 100kΩ merely by altering the value of R1 to 150kΩ, although results would probably be perfectly acceptable in practice without this modification.

Table 4.1. Components list for magnetic cartridge preamplifier

Resistors (all miniature ¼W, 5%)
R1	56kΩ
R2	120kΩ
R3	560Ω
R4	12kΩ
R5	220kΩ
R6	470kΩ
R7	8.2kΩ
R8	1kΩ

Capacitors
C1	470nF type C280
C2	6.8nF polystyrene
C3	15nF type C280
C4	10μF, 10V
C5	100μF, 10V
C6	1μF, 10V

Semiconductors
TR1	BC109C
TR2	BC109C

Switch
S1	S.P.S.T. toggle or miniature toggle type

Miscellaneous
metal case
0.1in matrix stripboard panel
input and output sockets
two PP3 batteries and connectors to suit
wire, solder, etc.
Note that two sets of components are required for a stereo preamplifier.

It is possible that some combinations of pickup and amplifier will need a higher gain than the preamplifier provides with the specified component values. Increased gain can be provided by reducing the value of R3, but this should not be reduced in value more than is absolutely necessary.

A problem which is often encountered when using equipment of this type is that of greatly increased mains hum. This can be due to stray pick-up if the circuit is not properly screened, and if screened leads are not employed at the input and output. However, the most likely cause is a hum loop. This can occur when a piece of equipment in the system is connected to the mains earth through more than one path, and so this point should be carefully checked so that all parts of the system are earthed through a single path.

5

Crystal Microphone Preamplifier

A low impedance dynamic microphone preamplifier was described earlier in this book, and it was pointed out then that this type of preamplifier is unsuitable for use with a crystal microphone. Crystal microphones have a higher output level than low impedance dynamic types (several millivolts), but they must operate into a very high impedance. A load impedance of at least 1MΩ is needed, and preferably the load impedance should be several times this level. Using a significantly lower load impedance results in a severe loss of bass response.

The reason for this is that a crystal microphone consists basically of a voltage generator in series with a low value capacitor. The value of this series capacitance will depend upon the make and model used, but is always something in the region of a few nanofarads. The impedance of this capacitance varies with applied frequency in the usual way, and is typically something like 1MΩ at 50Hz and 10kΩ at 5kHz. If the microphone were to be used into an impedance of say a few kilohms, then losses through the series capacitance would rapidly increase with decreasing frequency. This would result in severe attenuation of bass frequencies, and even some treble frequencies would be significantly attenuated.

By using an amplifier having an input impedance of a few megohms the losses through the series capacitance become negligible even at bass frequencies, and so the frequency response of the microphone is not adversely affected.

This series capacitance also makes it impossible to obtain satisfactory results using a crystal microphone direct into a long microphone lead. This is because the microphone lead has to be a screened cable, and has quite a high capacitance (usually several hundred picofarads per metre). This capacitance forms a capacitive divider in conjunction with series capacitance of the microphone, and losses through this divider circuit will be high if a long microphone lead (having high capacitance) is used.

23

Cable microphony, where any vibration in the cable produces an audio output, can also be troublesome on occasions. Both these problems can be greatly alleviated by using a suitable preamplifier close to the microphone so that the relatively low output impedance of the preamplifier feeds into the long microphone cable.

Few pieces of audio equipment have a suitable input for a crystal microphone (or any other type of microphone for that matter) and so require a preamp. such as this to provide the necessary interfacing. Note that a crystal microphone cannot be used successfully direct into a crystal or ceramic pick-up input as although these provide a high input impedance, the sensitivity is far too low. This preamplifier will match a crystal microphone to this type of input, or any similar high level input (*Tape, Tuner, Aux*, etc.).

The circuit

The circuit diagram of the crystal microphone preamplifier appears in Fig. 5.1. TR1 is used as the active element of the input stage, and it is used in the common emitter mode. However, it provides only a small amount of voltage gain as it has a fairly high value unbypassed emitter

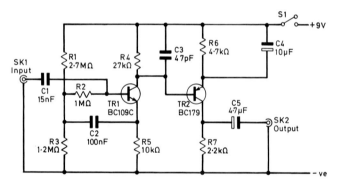

Figure 5.1

Circuit diagram of the crystal mic preamp.

resistor (R5). This has the effect of introducing a large amount of series negative feedback to the circuit which greatly boosts the input impedance of TR1. The input impedance is roughly equal to the value of R5 multiplied by the gain of TR1.

TR1 is a BC109C which has a typical current gain of 520 at a collector current of 2mA, which would give a typical input impedance of 5.2MΩ. This is not quite achieved in practice as TR1 is used at a somewhat lower collector current in order to obtain a low noise level, and this results in some reduction in its current gain. An input impedance of a few megohms is still obtained though.

Biasing for TR1 is provided by R1, R2 and R3. Bootstrapping is provided by capacitor C2, and this is needed in order to prevent the biasing resistor network from significantly shunting the input impedance of TR1. There is approximately unity gain between TR1 base and emitter, and so any change in the potential at TR1 base due to the input signal is matched by an almost identical change at TR1 emitter. This voltage change is coupled to the junction of R1, R2 and R3 by C2. Thus any change in the voltage at the right hand side of R2 is matched by an almost identical change at the other end, and so no significant input signal current flows through R2, which appears to have virtually an infinite impedance. In this way the shunting effect of the biasing resistors is almost totally eliminated.

C1 provides d.c. blocking at the input and R4 is the collector load resistor for TR1. C3 shunts R4 at high frequencies outside the audio range and provides high frequency roll off. This helps to maintain the stability of the circuit and also reduces the risk of strong radio transmissions being picked up.

TR2 is also used in the common emitter mode, but this has no a.c. negative feedback and is used at a comparatively high collector current so that it provides a high level of voltage gain. It is direct coupled to TR1 collector and it has R6 as its emitter bias resistor. R6 is bypassed by C4 so as to eliminate a.c. feedback here. R7 is the collector load for TR2 and C5 provides d.c. blocking at the output. S1 is an ordinary on/off switch.

The circuit has a current consumption of approximately 1mA from a 9V supply. The voltage gain of the amplifier is about 60 times, which should be adequate to match virtually any crystal microphone to any amplifier, mixer, etc. The unweighted signal to noise ratio of the circuit (input short circuited) is about − 57dB with reference to an output level of 500mV r.m.s.

Construction

It is virtually essential to build the unit into a metal case as the circuit has both high sensitivity and a high input impedance, and it is therefore extremely sensitive to mains hum, and pick up of others forms of electrical interference. A suitable component layout for the unit is shown in Fig. 5.2. This is based on a piece of 0.1in matrix stripboard which has 16 holes by 11 copper strips. Make the two breaks in the copper strips and drill the two mounting holes before soldering the components into position. It is a good idea to use screened leads to connect the panel to the input and output sockets, but this is not

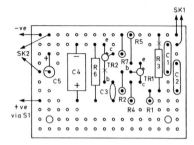

Figure 5.2

Component layout

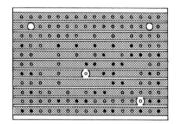

essential provided these two leads are kept fairly short and reasonably well apart from one another.

Using the unit

It may well be found that the circuit becomes unstable if it is used without a microphone plugged into the input. This can be cured by connecting a capacitor of about 100pF or so across the input socket, although it is not absolutely necessary as the instability will disappear as soon as a microphone is connected. Obviously though, it is advisable to add this capacitor (if necessary) if the unit is likely to be left switched on and connected to an amplifier without a microphone plugged in, as it is otherwise likely that a high level audio signal will be fed to the

26

amplifier which could be annoying, and could even result in damage to the amplifier or speaker. A fairly high noise level is to be expected when no microphone is connected to the unit, but this should greatly diminish when a microphone is plugged in.

Table 5.1. Components list for crystal microphone preamplifier

Resistors (all miniature ¼W, 5 or 10%)
R1	2.7MΩ
R2	1MΩ
R3	1.2MΩ
R4	27kΩ
R5	10kΩ
R6	4.7kΩ
R7	2.2kΩ

Capacitors
C1	15nF, type C280
C2	100nF, type C280
C3	47pF, ceramic plate
C4	10μF, 10V
C5	4.7μF, 10V

Semiconductors
TR1	BC109C
TR2	BC179

Switch
S1	S.P.S.T. toggle type or miniature toggle type

Miscellaneous
metal case
0.1in matrix stripboard panel
input and output sockets
PP3 battery and connector to suit
wire, solder, etc.

If the unit is used in conjunction with an amplifier it is likely that a howling sound will be produced when the volume control is advanced. This is due to acoustic feedback, and can be avoided by keeping the speaker and microphone well separated, and not advancing the volume control any more than is absolutely necessary.

6

Dynamic Noise Limiter

Small cassette recorders and players are extremely popular, probably because they offer a good compromise between portability and ruggedness on one hand, and performance on the other. For normal domestic use they have the drawback of providing rather limited volume though. This can be rectified by feeding the output from the unit into a hi-fi system, record player, or some other amplifier and speaker combination of reasonable power handling capability, so that the output from the unit is boosted somewhat.

However, if this is done it is likely that results will not be entirely satisfactory as the signal to noise ratio of most small cassette recorders is not very high. This is not normally too important as the noise level is not usually very noticeable on what is only a rather limited sound level anyway. When the volume is considerably boosted though, so too is the background noise level which then becomes very much more intrusive.

This background noise consists mainly of what is called 'tape noise' or 'tape hiss'. This consists of a wide range of audio frequencies, but it is the high frequencies which the listener finds most noticeable. The normal method of reducing this noise is to use the tone controls to provide a degree of treble cut. This attenuates the most objectionable part of the noise and gives an apparent large increase in the signal to noise ratio.

Obviously this method reduces treble signals at least as much as it reduces the noise, and in that respect is not entirely satisfactory. A better method is to use a dynamic treble cut filter where the amount of treble cut applied to the signal is dependent upon the amplitude of the signal.

This type of filter relies upon the fact that the tape noise is only noticeable on low level signals. High level signals mask the noise and thus render it inaudible. Therefore, if the signal is subjected to the treble cut when it is at a low level, but allowed to pass unaltered when it is at a high level, the tape hiss will still be apparently reduced, but there will be no loss of treble signals on high level signals. In this way the loss of treble signals is minimised, although admittedly there is still a loss of treble response on low level signals. This is unavoidable with a noise reduction system which operates only on playback.

The filter which is described here is of the type outlined above, and is designed for use between the earphone output of a small cassette recorder or player and the input of any amplifier which has a reasonably high input impedance and an output power of at least a few watts (a suitable amplifier design is described later).

The circuit

The circuit is very simple and employs just two active devices, as can be seen from the circuit diagram of the unit which appears in Fig. 6.1.

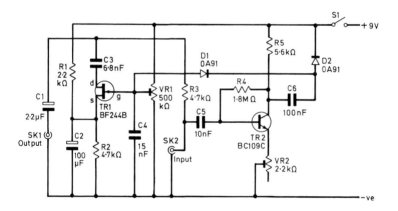

Figure 6.1

Circuit diagram of the dynamic noise limiter

Part of the input signal is coupled to the output socket via R3 and C1. TR1 is a junction gate field effect transistor (jugfet) and is used here as a voltage controlled resistance. Its source terminal is held about 6V or so above ground potential by the potential divider formed by R1 and R2, and C2 provides decoupling here. VR1 can be used to supply TR1 with a gate potential of anything between 0 and 9V, and in practice it is used to apply a small reverse bias to TR1. This bias is not sufficient to switch TR1 off, and so it exhibits a drain to source resistance of only about 100Ω.

This effectively connects the lower end of C3 to ground via TR1 and C2. C3 then forms a simple RC treble cut filter in conjunction with R3, and the necessary treble cut is applied to the signal as it passes from the input socket to the output socket.

Some of the input signal is applied to the input of a common emitter amplifier which utilises TR2. This stage is biased by R4 and has R5 as its collector load resistance. The variable resistance in the emitter circuit of TR2 is unbypassed and can therefore be used to apply a variable amount of negative feedback to this stage. In this way VR2 controls the voltage gain of TR2. The output from TR2 is coupled via C6 to a simple rectifier circuit which uses D1 and D2. The negative output from this circuit is connected to TR1 gate.

VR2 is adjusted so that with low level input signals the output voltage from the rectifier circuit is quite small and has no real effect on TR1. High level signals produce a much larger negative output bias though, and this has the effect of partially cutting TR1 off, or even completely cutting it off if the input signal is at a very high level. This means that C3 is either partially or completely cut out of circuit, with the treble cut being either partly or fully removed in consequence.

Thus the treble cut is applied to low level signals, but is removed on high level signals. C4 smoothes the output from the rectifier circuit so as to avoid causing distortion due to rapid changes in the gate voltage of TR1, but it provides a fairly fast time constant here so that the circuit responds quickly to changes in the input signal level.

The coupling capacitors used in the C5 and C6 positions have been given fairly low values so that low and middle frequency signals are attenuated in this part of the circuit. This makes the circuit respond more readily to treble frequencies than it does to bass and middle ones. It is normal to give circuits of this type such a bias as tape hiss is more readily masked by treble signals than it is by signals at lower frequencies.

The current consumption of the circuit is less than 1mA.

Construction

The components are assembled on a 0.1in matrix stripboard having 28 holes by 13 copper strips and the component layout is shown in Fig. 6.2. VR1 and VR2 must both be sub-miniature (sometimes described as 0.1W) horizontal presets if they are to fit into this layout.

D1 and D2 are germanium diodes and are therefore vulnerable to damage by overheating when they are being soldered into position. It is advisable to use a heatsink on each diode leadout wire as it is soldered into circuit, and these soldered joints should be made reasonably quickly. If a special heatshunt is not available, a pair of long nosed pliers can be used to grip the leadout close to the body of the diode as

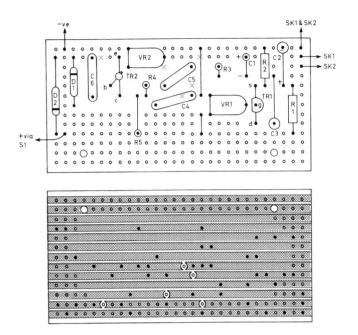

Figure 6.2

Component layout

it is soldered into position, and quite efficient heatshunting will be provided in this way.

Using the unit

The noise limiter circuit is fed from the earphone socket of the recorder via a twin lead which need not be screened as the output impedance of

31

the recorder will be very low, and the signal level in this lead is fairly high. The earphone output is nearly always a 3.5mm jack socket which is clearly marked, but this is not always the case and if in any doubt either the manual supplied with the recorder or the dealer from whom the unit was purchased should be consulted. Many recorders are fitted with a simple top-cut tone control, and if this is the case, set this control for maximum treble. The volume control on the recorder should be set to where it would be if the unit was being used in the normal way.

The output should be coupled to the amplifier input via a reasonably short screened lead. The amplifier can be any type which has an input

Table 6.1. Components list for dynamic noise limiter

Resistors (all miniature ¼W, 5 or 10%)	
R1	2.2kΩ
R2	4.7kΩ
R3	4.7kΩ
R4	1.8MΩ
R5	5.6kΩ
VR1	500kΩ (or 470kΩ) sub-miniature horizontal preset
VR2	2.2kΩ sub-miniature horizontal preset
Capacitors	
C1	2.2μF, 10V
C2	100μF, 6V
C3	6.8nF polystyrene
C4	15nF type C280
C5	10nF type C280
C6	100nF type C280
Semiconductors	
TR1	BF244B
TR2	BC109C
D1	OA91
D2	OA91
Switch	
S1	S.P.S.T. toggle or miniature toggle type
Miscellaneous	
metal case	
0.1in matrix stripboard panel	
input and output sockets	
PP3 battery and connector to suit	
wire, solder, etc.	

with a sensitivity of a few hundred millivolts and an input impedance of about 25kΩ or more. It is not advisable to use an amplifier having an input impedance much lower than 25kΩ as this impedance will be shunted across C3 in the noise limiter, with a consequent reduction in its effectiveness. If the amplifier is a stereo type the two inputs can be connected in parallel. An input for a crystal or ceramic pick-up is ideal for this application, but virtually all *Tape, Tuner, Aux.* and similar inputs will be suitable.

Initially VR1 should be set with its slider at about the centre of its track and VR2 should be adjusted to insert maximum resistance into circuit (set fully clockwise). If VR1 is adjusted backwards and forwards over its entire range of settings it should be possible to locate a small range of settings where the treble cut can be introduced or eliminated. VR1 should be set at the clockwise end of this range of setting so that the treble cut is applied to the processed signal, but would be eliminated by adjusting VR1 slightly in anticlockwise direction.

The best setting for VR2 must be found by trial and error. If it is set for too low a resistance the treble cut will only be partially lifted on high level signals or they may not be affected at all. On the other hand, setting it for too low a resistance will result in the treble cut being removed on low level signals, and this effect will be clearly audible. With a little experimentation it should be possible to locate a good compromise setting.

If required, the value of C3 can be altered to provide increased or decreased treble attenuation so as to better suit particular equipment and personal tastes. Raising its value increases the treble cut, and reducing its value has the opposite effect.

7

Miniature Power Amplifier

This miniature power amplifier uses a simple but reliable circuit which is based on the Motorola MC3360P integrated circuit. The unit is very versatile and can be used in such applications as a guitar practice amplifier, workshop amplifier, etc., as well as being suitable for use as an integral part of small pieces of audio and electronic equipment (radios, cassette players, etc.).

The use of an integrated circuit produces quite a high level of performance despite the simplicity of the design. The level of total harmonic distortion is typically less than 1% at most output powers. A maximum output power (without clipping) of about 250 to 300mW is available into a 15 or 16Ω loudspeaker. The input sensitivity of the unit is approximately 110mV into 10kΩ for maximum output, but this can be increased if necessary. The unweighted signal to noise ratio of the circuit is in excess of − 60dB.

The circuit

Fig. 7.1 shows the complete circuit diagram of the amplifier. The circuitry within the MC3360P i.c. is basically just a common emitter driver stage feeding a complementary emitter follower output stage. A small forward bias is applied to the output transistors under quiescent conditions so as to minimise crossover distortion in the usual way. Thermal stabilisation of this bias current is also provided so that the unit is protected against thermal runaway. This device is contained in a standard 8 pin DIL plastic package, but note that pins 2, 3, 6 and 7 are unused.

The emitters of the output transistors connect to pin 5, and the output signal is coupled from here to the loudspeaker via d.c. blocking capacitor C5. The positive and negative supplies connect to pins 8 and 4 respectively. The base of the driver transistor connects to pin 1, and this is direct coupled to the output of a discrete common emitter pre-amplifier stage which employs TR1. The emitter of this stage connects to the output terminal of the i.c., and this results in virtually 100% negative feedback being applied to the amplifier as a whole.

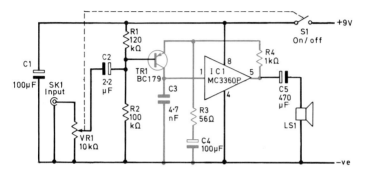

Figure 7.1

Circuit diagram. The i.c. is basically a common emitter driver stage feeding a complementary emitter follower output stage. The coloured circuit shows the negative feedback loop

This is very convenient from the point of view of circuit biasing, as the output should ideally be biased to about half the supply rail voltage. This permits the maximum possible output voltage swing to be obtained without one half of the output waveform being clipped. The negative feedback provides the circuit with a gain of about unity between TR1 base and pin 1 of I.C.1, and so the output can be biased to about half the supply potential by similarly biasing the base of TR1. This is accomplished by R1 and R2.

Of course, a gain of only unity at audio frequencies is of no practical use, and at a.c. some of the feedback must be removed in order to provide the circuit with a useful voltage gain. This is done by partially decoupling TR1 emitter using C4 and R3. C4 merely provides d.c. blocking, and R3 limits the amount of feedback that is decoupled. There is no point in completely removing the negative feedback as this would simply result in the circuit having a voltage gain which was excessive for most applications. Also, the negative feedback has the beneficial effect of reducing noise and distortion, and it is therefore a good idea to use as much feedback as possible.

By controlling the amount of feedback applied to the circuit at audio frequencies, R3 controls the gain of the circuit. The voltage gain of the circuit is approximately equal to R4 divided by R3, or 18 times with the specified values for these two components.

35

C2 provides d.c. blocking at the input and VR1 is the volume control. The latter is ganged with the *on/off* switch S1. C1 is a supply decoupling capacitor. C3 is needed in order to roll off the high frequency response of the circuit which would otherwise extend well into the radio frequency spectrum. This would be extremely undesirable as it would almost certainly lead to violent instability due to stray R.F. feedback between the input and output of the circuit.

The MC3360P has a class B output stage which has a quiescent current consumption of only about 3mA from a 9V supply. However, at high output volume levels the current consumption rises to about 40mA or so. It is therefore recommended that a fairly large capacity 9V battery such as a PP6 or PP7 should be used to power the amplifier.

Construction

A suitable 0.1in matrix stripboard layout for the amplifier is shown in Fig. 7.2. This is based on a board having 23 by 13 holes with the copper strips running lengthwise.

Construction of this panel is quite straightforward. There are only two breaks in the copper strips, and these should be made before the components are soldered into position. It is advisable to solder the i.c. into circuit after the other components have been connected, and it will be necessary to carefully bend the pins of the i.c. in slightly to get it to fit onto the panel. Don't omit the two link wires.

It is a good idea to use a continuity tester to check for accidental short circuits between adjacent copper strips due to minute drips of excess solder. Although only fairly modest powers are involved in this circuit, it is quite possible that such a short circuit could result in one of the semiconductor devices being damaged.

The amplifier (complete with battery, speaker and volume control/*on/off* switch) can easily be accommodated in a small metal or plastics case with the loudspeaker and VR1/S1 being mounted on the front panel. A circular cutout for the speaker must be made in the panel, and the diameter of the cutout should be about 20% less than the diameter of the speaker. Probably the most easy method of making this is to use a fretsaw or a coping saw. A piece of speaker fret or material should be glued in place behind the cutout using any good quality general purpose adhesive, and then the speaker can be glued in position onto the speaker material. Use only a small amount of adhesive and apply it only to the rim of the loudspeaker. Getting glue onto the diaphragm would almost certainly impair the quality of reproduction.

The integrated circuit is intended for use with loudspeakers having an impedance of about 15 or 16Ω, but unfortunately small speakers of a suitable impedance do not seem to be readily available. It is quite

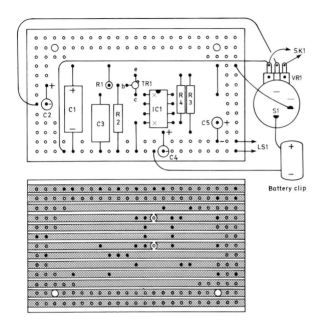

Figure 7.2

Component layout and wiring for V R1

acceptable to use a speaker of more than 16 ohms impedance, but the higher the speaker impedance the lower the maximum available output power becomes (approximately 180mW into 25Ω, 120mW into 40Ω, and 80mW into 75 or 80Ω). In practice it seems to be perfectly all right to use an 8Ω speaker, but a speaker of less than this impedance must not be used.

37

Using the amplifier

In order to minimise stray pick up of mains hum etc., a screened input lead should be used. The outer braiding of this cable connects to the negative supply rail of the amplifier.

In some applications where only a small input signal is available it will be necessary to increase the gain of the circuit in order to obtain an adequate volume level. This can be accomplished by reducing the value of R3. As explained earlier, the gain of the circuit is roughly equal to R4 divided by R3. About 2V r.m.s. is needed at the output for full output into a 15–16Ω loudspeaker, and so the input sensitivity of the circuit is given by 2 000 divided by (R4 divided by R3), and this gives an answer in millivolts r.m.s. Thus values of 39, 27, 15, and 10Ω for R3 give input sensitivities of about 78, 54, 30, and 20mV respectively.

Table 7.1. Components list for miniature power amplifier

Resistors (all miniature ¼W, 5%)	
R1	120kΩ
R2	100kΩ
R3	56Ω
R4	1kΩ
VR1	10kΩ log. with switch (S1)
Capacitors	
C1	100μF, 10V
C2	2.2μF, 10V
C3	4.7nF polystyrene, etc.
C4	100μF, 10V
C5	470μF, 10V
Semiconductors	
TR1	BC179
I C.1	MC3360P
Miscellaneous	
metal or plastics cabinet	
0.1in matrix stripboard panel	
PP6 battery and connector to suit	
control knob	
input socket	
8 to 80Ω impedance loudspeaker (see text)	
wire, solder, etc.	

It is recommended that R3 should not be made much less than 10Ω as this would result in a considerable increase in noise and distortion, and it is also likely that instability would result. If the output signal level of the equipment from which the amplifier is being fed is unknown, it is of course possible to find the best value for R3 by empirical means. The best value is the highest one which gives adequate sensitivity.

8

Quasi-quadraphonic Adapter

True quadraphonic equipment tends to be rather expensive and requires special recordings in order to produce the proper effect. Quite a good quadraphonic effect can be obtained using various types of quadraphonic synthesiser, of which the Hafler is the most popular. This type of quadraphonic adapter can be used in conjunction with an ordinary stereo system and an additional pair of speakers to provide quite realistic and interesting effects. No special quadraphonic records are required, and it is relatively inexpensive to use add-on equipment of this kind. Results will not be quite as good as those obtained with proper quadraphonic equipment, of course.

With the Hafler system, a rear speaker is fed with the difference signal which is obtained from the ordinary stereo signal; the latter being fed to the front speakers in the normal manner. Most practical systems use a slightly modified arrangement where the difference signal is fed to two rear speakers in antiphase, as this provides a slightly more realistic effect. Quadraphonic adapters of this type are often passive devices, but these suffer from practical drawbacks and there are advantages in using an active circuit which gives far greater control over the rear channels, and does not have any adverse effect on the main stereo amplifier.

The unit described here is a simple differential amplifier which will generate antiphase difference signals which can be fed to an additional stereo amplifier which in turn feeds the rear speakers. A suitable stereo amplifier will be found elsewhere in this book, although good results should be obtained by feeding the output from the adapter into the *Tape, Tuner,* or *Aux.* input of any stereo amplifier. The unit obtains its input from the *Tape* or *Aux.* output of the main amplifier.

The circuit

The circuit diagram of the adapter appears in Fig. 8.1. This is really just a conventional differential amplifier. Both transistors are biased from the potential divider formed by R1 and R2. R7, R8 and C1 are needed in order to provide a degree of isolation between the bases of TR1 and TR2.

An input signal applied to the base of TR1 appears inverted at TR1 collector with TR1 operating in the common emitter mode. It also

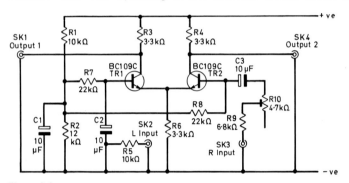

Figure 8.1

Quasi-quadraphonic adapter circuit diagram

appears in-phase at TR2 collector as TR1 also operates in the emitter follower mode with the signal appearing at its emitter. From here it is transferred to TR2 emitter and then to TR2 collector with TR2 operating in the common base mode to this emitter signal. By a similar process a signal applied to TR2 base appears inverted at TR2 collector and in phase at TR1 collector.

If identical input signals are applied to both inputs simultaneously there will be no output at either collector. This is because the input signal to TR1 base causes a change in the potential at the emitters of TR1 and TR2. This nullifies the input at TR2 base as any change in base potential here will be matched by an identical change in emitter potential. There is thus no change in the base-emitter potential of TR2, and so its collector voltage remains unaltered. The signal at TR2 base cancels out the signal at TR1 base in precisely the same manner.

If the input signals were out of phase, then the signal amplitude at each collector would be twice as high as it would be with an input connected to only one input. This is because the inter-reaction at the emitters would then increase the variations in base-emitter voltages, rather than cancel them out as in the previous example.

This circuit therefore produces an output which is proportional to the difference in the two input signals. Furthermore, there are the required two antiphase outputs.

In a practical situation, signals which appear one side of the sound stage will be present at the outputs of the circuit. Those signals which comprise the centre of the sound stage will be fed in phase to both inputs and will be cancelled out or partially cancelled at least. Of more importance are the random signals which will have been accidentally put onto the recording. These are signals which will often be picked up by a microphone after they have bounced around the walls and ceiling of the room in which the original performance took place. They will lag slightly behind the main signal and will be randomly phased. Some of this signal content will therefore be fed to the inputs of the differential amplifier in antiphase, and will emerge from the outputs at a comparatively high level. When fed to speakers situated to the rear of the listener this gives an audio system greatly enhanced ambience and realism.

The basic differential amplifier is not perfect and there is inevitably some difference in the sensitivities at the two inputs. R10 can be adjusted to compensate for this and thus optimise the cancelling effect of the circuit.

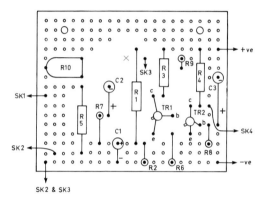

Figure 8.2

Stripboard layout (X indicates a break in the copper strip)

Construction

The circuit is constructed on a piece of 0.1 in pitch stripboard which has 16 copper strips by 20 holes. The component layout for this panel is shown in Fig. 8.2. Be careful not to omit the single break in the copper strips (between R10 and R9).

Construction of the unit can take two basic forms: it can either be built as a self-contained unit for use with an existing amplifier, or it can be housed in the same case as a purpose built amplifier.

If the former is the preferred method, the unit may be housed in a small metal instrument case and powered from a small 9V battery such as a PP3 via an S.P.S.T. *on/off* switch. Dual phono sockets or some similar type of socket can be used at the inputs and outputs. The connections to both stereo amplifiers should be made via reasonably short screened leads.

If the unit is built into a complete adapter including a stereo amplifier it can be powered from the same supply line as the amplifier, provided this line is reasonably well smoothed and is between about 9 and 20V. The *on/off* switch for the unit will then obviously be shared with the one used for the amplifier. The input leads should still be screened, but presumably the output leads will only be short and need not be screened.

Using the adapter

The normal loudspeaker placement for a quadraphonic system is with one speaker in each of the four corners of a square, with the listener(s) at the centre of the square. It is preferable for the distance between adjacent speakers to be about 2½ metres or more. Other effective loudspeaker placements are possible and there is plenty of room for experiment here.

It is not necessary for the rear speakers of a quasi-quadraphonic system to be of the same type as those used in the front channels. It is not even necessary for them to be of approximately equal quality, and it is quite normal to use comparatively inexpensive speakers in the rear channels. Provided the rear speakers are reasonably efficient types it is not necessary for the rear channel amplifier to have anything like the power of main amplifier, particularly if this is a high power type. One reason for this is that powerful stereo amplifiers are normally used with very inefficient speakers, and are not used at anything like full output even on volume peaks. Another reason is that the rear channels will be called upon to handle lower power levels than the front channels anyway.

Quite a good quadraphonic effect will be obtained with the outputs of the adapter connected either way round to the amplifier inputs.

However, for best results signals in the left hand front channel should produce in phase signals in the left hand rear speaker and out of phase signals in the right hand rear signal. Similarly, right hand front channel signals should be in phase at the right hand rear speaker and out of phase at the left rear speaker.

Probably the easiest way of finding the correct phasing is to disconnect the speakers for one side, say the right hand side. Then play something having plenty of bass content through the system while trying the system first with output 1 of the adapter connected to the left hand rear input, and then with output 2 so connected. One method of connection should produce a much more full bass response than the

Table 8.1. Components list for quasi-quadraphonic adapter

Resistors (all miniature, ¼W, 5%)	
R1	10kΩ
R2	12kΩ
R3	3.3kΩ
R4	3.3kΩ
R5	10kΩ
R6	3.3kΩ
R7	22kΩ
R8	22kΩ
R9	6.8kΩ
R10	4.7kΩ sub-miniature horizontal preset
Capacitors	
C1	10μF, 10V
C2	10μF, 10V
C3	10μF, 10V
Semiconductors	
TR1	BC109C
TR2	BC109C
Switch	
S1	S.P.S.T. toggle or miniature toggle type, if required (see text)
Miscellaneous	
metal case	
0.1in matrix stripboard panel	
input and output sockets	
PP3 battery and connector to suit if required (see text)	
wire, solder, etc.	

other, and this is the correct one. The remaining output then connects to the right rear input.

It is possible that some amplifiers will have a fairly high tape output amplitude which will result in the adapter being overloaded at high volume levels. If this should occur, it can be remedied by a tenfold increase in the values of R5, R9 and R10.

The easiest way of finding the correct setting for R10 is to play a mono signal through the system and then adjust this component for minimum rear channel output.

9

Three-channel Stereo Mixer

The ability to mix audio signals is a requirement of several fields in the general sphere of audio, the two most obvious examples being tape recording and the production of electronic music. The mixer featured here has three stereo inputs with separate level controls for the left and right channels to facilitate channel balancing, etc.

The input impedances are all approximately $47k\Omega$, and the gain of the circuit is unity. The input sensitivity is therefore equal to the required output level. The signal to noise ratio of the circuit is excellent with the output noise level being only about $100\mu V$. The unit incorporates a mono/stereo switch, and in the mono mode the unit operates as a six-channel mono mixer.

As described here the unit is only a rather basic mixer design, but it can be used with other circuits provided in this book to provide a much more sophisticated unit. For example, it can be used in conjunction with the peak level indicator circuit which is described later on, or the preamplifiers described previously.

The circuit

Fig. 9.1 shows the complete circuit schematic for the three-channel stereo mixer. Most mixers used to use a simple passive mixing circuit followed by an amplifier to compensate for losses in the mixing circuit, but these days the active mixer configuration used here has gained considerable popularity. It employs operational amplifier techniques.

The left and right hand channel circuits are basically identical, with I.C.1 being used in the left hand channel and I.C.2 in the right hand channel. R4 and R5 form a potential divider which is used to bias the non-inverting (+) input of both i.c.s to about half the supply rail potential. Any ripple on the supply lines must not be fed to the non-inverting inputs via this potential divider as this would result in the ripple being transferred to the i.c. outputs. C4 is therefore used to provide decoupling here.

Both channels of the unit operate in the same manner, and we will consider the left hand channel here. R6 is connected between the inverting input and the output of the i.c. and it thus provides a negative feedback. An operational amplifier is a form of differential amplifier and so the output voltage is equal to the voltage across the inputs multiplied by the voltage gain of the i.c. (which for an operational amplifier is theoretically infinite, and in practice the voltage gain is extremely high being typically 200,000 times for a 741C). The effect of the feedback is to stabilise the inverting input at the same voltage as the non-inverting input.

Each of the three inputs is fed to the i.c. input via an individual level control, d.c. blocking capacitor, and series resistor. If, for example, input 1 is taken 100mV positive, this will take the inverting input positive and will generate a voltage difference across the inputs of the i.c. This will cause the output to swing negative in order to feed a signal via R6 to the inverting input which will balance the inputs once again. As the series input resistors have a value which is the same as that of R6 the output will obviously have to swing 100mV negative in order to balance the input signal.

If each of the three inputs is taken 100mV positive then the output will have to swing 300mV negative in order to counteract the combination of the three inputs. In this way the circuit provides the required voltage adding action.

What is termed a 'virtual earth' is formed at the inverting input of the i.c. In a conventional operational amplifier circuit there are dual balanced power supplies with a central earthed supply rail. For convenience a single supply is used here with the central rail being produced by R4 and R5. The non-inverting input is connected to this rail and the inverting input is maintained at the same potential as the non-inverting one by the negative feedback action. Hence the term virtual earth, as the inverting input is maintained at earth potential. This virtual earth input provides the necessary isolation between the inputs.

Output d.c. blocking is provided by C5 and C6. The right hand channel mixer has an additional input resistor (R7) which can be connected to the left hand channel output by closing S1. When this is done the left hand output is mixed into the right hand input, and the unit then operates as a six channel mono mixer with all six inputs being present at the right hand channel output.

S2 is the ordinary *on/off* switch. The current consumption of the mixer is only about 2mA from a 9V supply.

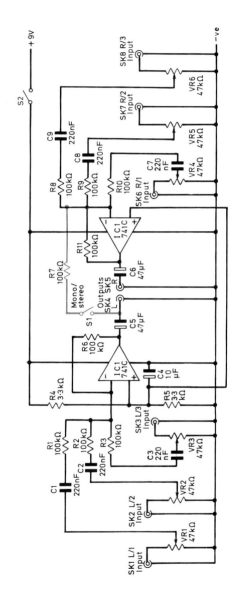

Figure 9.1

Circuit diagram of the mixer. When S1 is closed the unit operates as a six channel mono mixer

47

Construction

Apart from the controls, the circuit is built on a 0.1in pitch stripboard panel which has 22 copper strips by 29 holes with the components arranged as shown in Fig. 9.2. Be careful not to omit any of the 20 breaks in the copper strips or any of the 8 link wires. Also make sure that none of the copper strips are shorted together by excess solder, especially at the i.c.s and other points where the connections are rather crammed together.

As far as mechanical construction is concerned, probably the most practical solution is to use a sloping front type case with the controls and input sockets mounted on the front panel. The output sockets can be situated at the rear of the case. The obvious way of arranging the six level controls is in three groups of two with the left and right hand sliders for each channel being grouped together, with the left hand slider on the left and the right hand one on the right, of course. This is a very practical arrangement, particularly when slider potentiometers are being used, as it enables the level control settings to be seen at a glance. However, other arrangements can be used if preferred, and although slider potentiometers have been specified, ordinary rotary types are also suitable.

The slider potentiometers are logarithmic types and they must therefore be connected into circuit the right way round. If the slider is set at the centre of its track and an ohm meter is used to measure the resistance between the slider connection and the track ends, the two resistances will be extremely unequal. There will be quite a low resistance to one end of the track, and this is the end which connects to earth.

Mounting slider potentiometers can be something of a problem, and one method of making the necessary slot for each control knob shaft is to drill a line of small closely spaced holes where each cutout is to be made. These can then be joined up using a miniature round file, and a small flat file can be used to tidy up any rough edges on the slots. Most slider potentiometers have provision for mounting by two M3 screws. Quite a neat finish can be produced by using countersunk mounting screws and then fitting a ready-made self adhesive bezel over each cutout. An alternative method of mounting the potentiometers is to use a good quality general purpose adhesive.

Using the unit

Most tape recorders, tuners, tone generators, etc. will be capable of driving the mixer inputs directly. If the unit is to be employed as a microphone mixer it will be necessary to add suitable preamplifiers,

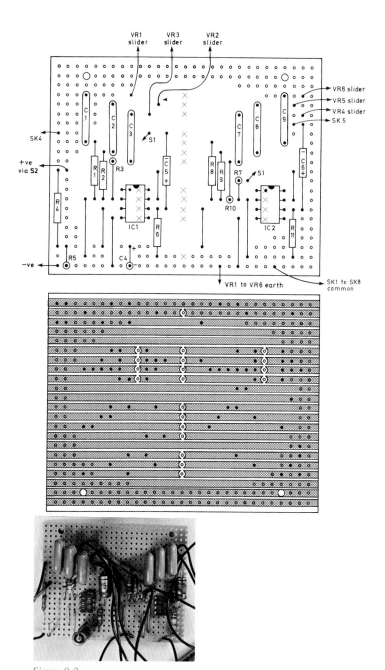

Figure 9.2

The component layout of the mixer

49

and suitable designs have already been covered in this book. A magnetic pickup will also need a suitable preamplifier, and the unit described earlier may be used. Alternatively, it is also possible to use the relevant part of a hi-fi amplifier by connecting the pick-up to the appropriate input and extracting the output for the mixer from the tape output of the amplifier.

Table 9.1. Components list for three-channel stereo mixer

Resistors (all miniature, ¼W, 5%)	
R1, R2, R3, R6, R7, R8, R9, R10 and R11	100kΩ (9 off)
R4 and R5	3.3kΩ (2 off)
VR1 to VR6	47kΩ log. slider potentio-meters (6 off)
Capacitors	
C1, C2, C3, C7, C8 and C9	220nF type C280 (six off)
C4	10μF, 10V
C5 and C6	4.7μF, 10V (2 off)
Semiconductors	
I.C.1	741C
I.C.2	741C
Switches	
S1	S.P.S.T. toggle or slider type
S2	S.P.S.T. toggle or slider type
Miscellaneous	
case	
0.1in matrix stripboard panel	
six slider potentiometer control knobs	
PP3 battery and connector to suit	
input and output sockets	
wire, solder, etc.	

Before putting the finished mixer into service it is advisable to check that the controls have been wired up correctly by making sure that each slider controls the channel it is supposed to, and only that channel. The unit will handle output levels of up to about 1V without clipping, but the overload margin can be considerably increased, if required, by raising the supply voltage. The supply voltage should not be more than about 30V (36V absolute maximum).

10

Slave Amplifier

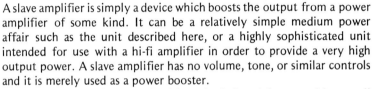

A slave amplifier is simply a device which boosts the output from a power amplifier of some kind. It can be a relatively simple medium power affair such as the unit described here, or a highly sophisticated unit intended for use with a hi-fi amplifier in order to provide a very high output power. A slave amplifier has no volume, tone, or similar controls and it is merely used as a power booster.

The slave amplifier described here is designed for use with a small transistor radio or cassette recorder. The output power and hence volume level available from these is rather limited for use in most domestic situations, and this unit will enable a much more realistic volume level to be obtained. It will provide a maximum output power of approximately 4 to 5W r.m.s. into an 8Ω speaker. Results obtained with the prototype unit are surprisingly good, especially when the unit is employed with an f.m. radio or a cassette recorder and the dynamic noise filter described earlier.

The circuit

The slave amplifier circuit diagram is given in Fig. 10.1. This consists basically of a common emitter Darlington pair driver stage using TR1 and TR2, and a complementary emitter follower output stage using TR3 and TR4.

The circuit must be biased so that about half the supply rail potential appears at the output of the amplifier (TR3 and TR4 emitters). The output transistors are used in the emitter follower mode and therefore have unity voltage gain. The Darlington pair must be biased in order to produce about half the supply voltage at TR1 and TR2 collectors in order to produce the correct output potential. This biasing is provided by R1 and R2. About 1.3V is needed at the base of TR1 in order to make TR1 and TR2 switch on fairly heavily, and so the bias resistors are given values which produce 1.3V at TR1 base with half the supply voltage present at the output. A negative feedback action then stabilises the circuit potentials at about the correct levels. R1 connects to the

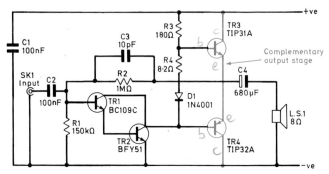

Figure 10.1

Slave amplifier circuit

output of the amplifier as a whole rather than to TR1 and TR2 collectors so that negative feedback is applied to the entire amplifier. The circuit uses a considerable amount of negative feedback and this produces low distortion and noise levels. In fact, compared with the noise and distortion present on the input signal the levels introduced by the slave amplifier will probably be negligible.

With a complementary output stage of this type, the *npn* transistor (TR3) conducts on positive-going output excursions and the *pnp* transistor (TR4) conducts on negative-going excursions. Although the output transistors provide no voltage gain, they do provide current amplification and act as an impedance converter which enables the loudspeaker to be directly driven from the output of circuit without the need for a matching transformer. C4 provides d.c. blocking at the output.

R3 is the main collector load resistance for the driver stage. R4 and D1 are inserted in the driver stage collector circuit to provide a small forward bias to the output transistors under quiescent conditions. About 1.2V is needed between the bases of the output transistors before they will begin to conduct, and R1 plus D1 provide such a voltage. D1 is connected so that it is forward biased and produces a voltage of about 0.5V. The remaining voltage is developed across R4. Without the bias provided by these components, signals of less than 1.2V peak to peak at TR1 collector would fail to produce any change in the output potential. Signals of more than 1.2V peak to peak would have the leading and trailing part of each half-cycle removed. This would result in severe distortion (known as crossover distortion).

52

D.C. blocking at the input is provided by C2, and C1 is a supply decoupling capacitor. C3 rolls off the high frequency response of the amplifier by applying increased feedback at these frequencies. This prevents the circuit from becoming unstable.

The voltage gain of the circuit is approximately equal to (R1 plus R2) divided by R1, which works out at about 8 times with the specified values. An output of around 6V r.m.s. is needed to produce full output from the amplifier, and so an input level of only about 750mV r.m.s. is needed to drive the circuit fully. Assuming the radio or recorder from which the amplifier is driven has the usual 8Ω speaker impedance, this means it needs to be capable of an output power of at least 70mW r.m.s. if it is to provide adequate drive for the slave amplifier. Virtually every radio and cassette recorder is capable of this.

Construction

All the components including the output transistors are mounted on a 0.1in matrix stripboard panel which has 12 copper strips by 20 holes. The wiring diagram for this is given in Fig. 10.2. This is mostly quite straightforward, but make quite sure that neither the seven breaks in the copper strips nor the single link wire is accidentally omitted. The ends of the leadout wires of TR3 and TR4 are bent downwards at right angles so that these components are mounted horizontally. The leadout wires of these components are quite thick, but they should just about fit into the holes of the panel.

It is absolutely essential to make sure that no mistakes are made when wiring up the panel, as a very simple error could easily result in the destruction of expensive components. Check the wiring thoroughly two or three times. In particular, make quite sure that D1 is connected with the correct polarity. Its cathode (the lead which emerges from the end of the component body which is marked with a white band) connects to the same copper strip as TR1 and TR2 collectors and TR4 base. If D1 should be connected with the wrong polarity the output transistors would draw an extremely high current when the supply is connected and could possibly be destroyed. It is a good idea to check for short circuits between adjacent copper strips using a continuity tester.

TR3 and TR4 must be mounted on a substantial heatsink as they will otherwise overheat and be destroyed. If the unit is fitted into a metal case it will probably be possible to find a way of employing this as the heatsink. If necessary, the output transistors can be secured to the case via a suitable mounting bracket fabricated from aluminium sheet. Alternatively they can be mounted on a medium or large size commercially produced heatsink.

In either case they must be electrically insulated from the heatsink using mica washer and plastic bush insulating sets. Mounting this type of transistor is quite simple as they each require only a single mounting hole. The mica washers fit between the metal pad on the underside of

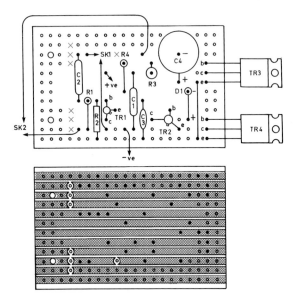

Figure 10.2

Stripboard layout

the transistor and the heatsink. Make sure that the mounting hole in the heatsink does not have any rough edges as these would be likely to penetrate the mica washer. The plastic bush fits into the mounting hole in the transistor (from above) and insulates the metal pad from the mounting bolt. M3 and 6B.A. mounting bolts can be used.

54

Use a continuity tester to check that the transistors are properly insulated from the heatsink. The metal pads of the transistors connect to their collector terminals, and so faulty insulation here could easily result in a short circuit on the supply rails.

The obvious form for the unit to take is as a self-contained unit complete with power supply and speaker. However, there is no reason why the unit should not be used with an external speaker if a suitable unit is available. The speaker should have an impedance of 8Ω and must be capable of handling at least 5W r.m.s.

The unit requires a supply voltage of about 20 to 24V. The amplifier has a class B output stage which draws a current of about 700mA at high volume levels, and even the quiescent current is something in the region of 60mA. This makes battery powered operation rather impracticable, and a mains power supply is required. A suitable unit is described at the end of this book.

Using the unit

The earphone socket of the recorder or radio is connected to the input socket of the amplifier via a two way lead terminated in suitable plugs.

Table 10.1. Components list for the slave amplifier

Resistors (all miniature ¼W, 5% except R3)
R1	150kΩ
R2	1MΩ
R3	180Ω, 1W
R4	8.2Ω

Capacitors
C1	100nF type C280
C2	100nF type C280
C3	10pF ceramic
C4	680µF, 16V

Semiconductors
TR1	BC109C
TR2	BFY51
TR3	TIP31A
TR4	TIP32A
D1	1N4001

Miscellaneous
metal, plastics or wooden case
0.1in matrix stripboard panel
input socket
8Ω loudspeaker capable of handling about 5W r.m.s.
wire, solder, etc.
heatsink and insulating sets for output transistors

Radios and cassette recorders have low impedance outputs and so the connecting cable can be quite long and need not be a screened type. The volume is controlled by the colume control on the radio or cassette recorder.

11

Audio Limiter

An audio limiter is a circuit which prevents an audio signal from exceeding some predetermined level. It can, for example, be used ahead of a tape recorder which is being used to record live music, or something of this nature. When making this type of recording it is not possible to guarantee that the recording level will not be exceeded at high volume levels unless the recording level controls are set well back. This is almost certain to produce a poor signal to noise ratio.

An audio limiter used between the mixer and the recorder can overcome this problem. The limiter is adjusted so that it comes into operation on input signals which exceed the maximum recording level, and it then provides sufficient attenuation to produce an output signal which is equal to the maximum recording level. The circuit is a sort of automatic volume control which reduces the signal by the appropriate amount if it senses an overload, and in this way it prevents serious distortion.

The unit has uses in applications other than tape recording and it can be used with a guitar amplifier, disco amplifier, etc. to ensure that overloading and consequent output clipping do not occur. It can also be used in low and medium fidelity tape recording as an automatic recording level control, and circuits of this type are often employed in communications systems. There are probably many other possible uses for the unit.

The circuit

This appears in Fig. 11.1, and is based on a voltage controlled attenuator which is formed by R3 and TR1. The source terminal of TR1 is held about 6V positive by the potential divider formed by R1 and R2. Decoupling at TR1 source is provided by C2. TR1 gate is normally tied to the negative supply rail potential by R4, and so TR1 is heavily reverse biased under static conditions. This means that TR1 is normally cut off and has a drain to source resistance of many megohms. TR1 therefore has no shunting effect on the signal flowing through R3. This signal is coupled to the output socket via an emitter follower stage which uses

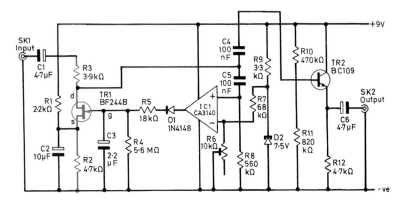

Figure 11.1

The circuit diagram of the audio limiter. R3 and TR1 act as a voltage controlled attenuator

TR2. The purpose of this stage is to act as a high-input-impedance buffer which ensures that loading of the output does not have a significant shunting effect on the signal through R3.

I.C.1 is an operational amplifier, but it is used here as a comparator. The inverting (−) input of I.C.1 is fed with a reference voltage which is derived from a zener stabilised supply rail. This voltage can be adjusted to anything from zero to about 1V by means of R6. The non-inverting (+) input of the i.c. is ground referenced by R8.

R6 is adjusted so that the voltage at the inverting input of the i.c. is equal to the maximum peak output voltage which is acceptable. With the non-inverting input then at a lower voltage than the inverting input of the i.c., the output of the device goes to a very low potential. The signal from TR1 drain is coupled to the non-inverting input of the i.c. by C5, and on positive going half cycles this signal will take the non-inverting input positive of the inverting one if there is an overload.

If this should happen, the output of the i.c. will swing to virtually the positive supply rail voltage for the period when the peak overload level is exceeded. This generates a series of positive pulses at the output

58

of the i.c., and these are fed to the gate of TR1 through D1 and R5. These pulses place a positive charge on C3, and this results in TR1 being turned on to some degree. This in turn reduces its drain to source resistance considerably so that the signal at TR1 is reduced in amplitude and the overloading is counteracted.

The circuit operates less than instantaneously as R5 limits the speed at which C3 can be charged from the output of I.C.1. This is necessary as a tighter coupling between I.C.1 output and TR1 gate would result in large and rapid changes in the potential at TR1 gate, and this would cause severe distortion. The attack time of the circuit is still quite short though. The circuit will not respond to very brief and minor overloads, but these are unlikely to produce noticeable distortion anyway.

The circuit has hysteresis, which means that it responds quite quickly to overloads, but takes somewhat longer to return to normal once the overload has been removed. This is an essential feature as the circuit would otherwise become rather unstable, and could also generate large amounts of distortion. The hysteresis is introduced by D1 which enables C3 to be quickly charged from the low impedance output of the i.c. through the relatively low impedance of R5, but blocks the discharge path in the opposite direction. Instead, C3 must discharge through the comparatively high impedance of R4.

Construction

The unit is constructed on a stripboard which has 13 copper strips by 27 holes using the component layout illustrated in Fig. 11.2. Make the 15 breaks in the copper strips before soldering the components into position.

I.C.1 has a PMOS input stage, and the input terminals can be damaged by high static voltages. This device has internal protection circuitry though, and so it is not easily damaged in this way. The device will probably be supplied in some form of protective packaging, such as conductive foam, and *it is advisable to leave it in this packaging until it is time to solder it into position.* I.C.1 should be the last component to be connected, and it should be handled as little as possible once it has been removed from the protective packing.

The CA3140 is available in two common forms; the CA3140T and the CA3140S. Both are housed in an ordinary 8 pin TO–99 package, but the 'T' version has straight leadout wires, whereas those of the 'S' version are formed into the standard op. amp. I.C. 8 pin DIL configuration. Either version will readily fit into this component layout.

The unit can be built as a completely self contained unit with input and output sockets, an internal 9V battery supply, and an *on/off* switch,

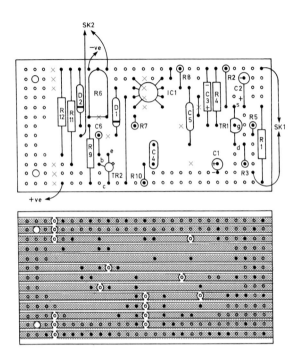

Figure 11.2
Layout of the limiter

but in many instances it will be possible and preferable to build it into existing equipment. The current consumption of the unit is approximately 4mA from a 9V supply.

60

Theoretically R6 can be adjusted for any limiting level of between zero and about 2V peak to peak. In practice though, the limits are a few hundred millivolts peak to peak and a few volts peak to peak. Assuming that the unit is to be used at the input of a tape recorder, the easiest method of giving R6 the correct adjustment is to feed a strong input signal into the unit (so that the limiting action is produced), and then

Table 11.1. Components list for the audio limiter

Resistors (all miniature, ¼W 5 or 10%)
R1	2.2kΩ
R2	4.7kΩ
R3	3.9kΩ
R4	5.6MΩ
R5	18kΩ
R6	10kΩ sub-miniature horizontal preset
R7	68kΩ
R8	560kΩ
R9	3.3kΩ
R10	470kΩ
R11	820kΩ
R12	4.7kΩ

Capacitors
C1	4.7μF, 10V
C2	10μF, 10V
C3	2.2μF, 10V
C4	100nF type C280
C5	100nF type C280
C6	4.7μF, 10V

Semiconductors
TR1	BF244B
TR2	BC109
I.C 1	CA3140T or CA3140S
D1	1N4148
D2	BZY88C7V5 (7.5V 400mW zener)

Miscellaneous
metal case, if required (see text)
0.1in matrix stripboard panel
PP3 battery, connector to suit, S.P.S.T. toggle switch (S1), input and
    output sockets, if required (see text)
connecting wire, solder, etc.

simply adjust R6 for the highest output level which does not produce an overload on the recording level indicators of the recorder. It should be possible to devise similar methods if the unit is used with other types of equipment.

When tested with an audio signal generator the unit provided almost perfect results with virtually no increase in the output level when the input signal was taken well above the limiting threshold. Of course, practical signals are much more complex and results may not be quite as good on such signals, although they should still be excellent. Gross overloads will saturate the f.e.t. and partially defeat the limiting action, and so the unit cannot be expected to handle an extremely large dynamic range. It will comfortably handle a 20dB overload, and this is more than is likely to occur in a practical situation.

In hi-fi applications a unit such as this is used as a sort of insurance policy which will, hopefully, rarely come into operation. It is undesirable for it to do so as this results in some distortion of the dynamic levels. However, this is preferable to the ordinary forms of distortion which occur if an overload is allowed to pass unchecked. In low and medium fidelity applications, such as the taping of a discussion, the unit can be fed with a fairly strong signal so that the limiting action will be brought into action much of the time. This will compress the dynamic range of the output signal, thus preventing overloading on strong signals and boosting weak signals which would otherwise tend to drop down into the background noise level.

12

Stereo Peak Level Indicator

A peak level indicator is rather like a simplified version of an audio limiter (as described previously). Instead of automatically compensating for a detected overload, a peak level indicator provides a visual indication of the presence of an overload.

It can be useful to have a peak level indicator in addition to an ordinary VU meter, and many cassette recorders have this feature these days. Meters have a comparatively slow response and they are likely to fail to indicate overloads of a very brief and intermittent nature, such as those caused by a very spiky waveform. Peak level indicators have an extremely fast response time and will therefore detect and indicate the presence of such overloads.

Apart from use in conjunction with VU meters, peak level indicators are now widely used on their own in equipment such as disco amplifiers, mixers, etc., where the use of expensive VU meters is not always completely justified.

The unit described here is intended for stereo operation, with an overload on either channel being indicated by a light emitting diode. It would be quite possible to have separate l.e.d.s for the two stereo channels, but it is more usual to have an indicator lamp which is common to both channels. The unit does actually have two l.e.d. indicators, but these are common to both channels and provide monitoring of any two levels which are 3dB apart. This is much more useful than having just a single indicator with monitoring at one level, particularly if the unit is not used together with VU meters, as the lower level indicator gives warning of a likely overload. A single indicator only provides indication of an actual overload.

The circuit

The simplified circuit diagram of the unit is provided in Fig. 12.1. This shows the circuit for one channel, but some components are common to both channels.

The circuit is based on a Motorola MC3302P quad comparator i.c. The non-inverting (+) inputs of the comparators are fed with a reference voltage which is derived from a zener stabilised supply. Two of the comparators are fed with the voltage produced by R3 and R4, and the other two are fed with the potential produced by R6 and R7.

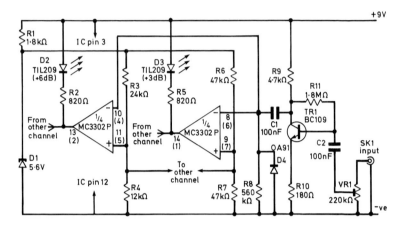

Figure 12.1

Simplified circuit of the peak level indicator. Only one channel is shown, although some components are common to both

The input signal is fed to the inverting (−) inputs of the comparators. The inverting inputs are referenced to ground by R8, and the non-inverting inputs are therefore at the higher potential. This causes the comparator outputs to go high. A light emitting diode (l.e.d.) is connected between the outputs and the positive supply rail. There are actually two l.e.d.s, one to indicate the lower level and the other to indicate a level 3dB higher. The equivalent left and right hand channels are connected in parallel so that each indicator is common to both channels. With the comparator outputs high there will be no voltage developed across the l.e.d.s and they will not come on.

On positive input peaks of adequate amplitude the inverting inputs will be taken positive of the non-inverting ones and the outputs will go low for the period that this occurs. This results in a current being supplied to the l.e.d.s via their current limiting resistors (R2 and R5) and so the l.e.d.s light up.

R3 and R4 produce a reference voltage which is one third higher than that produced by R6 and R7. Therefore, an input level which is just sufficient to cause D3 to come on will not switch on D2; it would need to be increased in amplitude by one third (3dB) before it would do so. In this way the circuit provides indications at two levels 3dB apart, regardless of what these actual levels are.

The basic sensitivity of the circuit is not very high, and so a common emitter amplifier is used at each input to boost the sensitivity. Only about 100mV r.m.s. is needed at the input in order to bring both l.e.d.s on, but the sensitivity of each channel can be reduced to the appropriate level by means of the preset sensitivity controls (VR1 and VR1a). The input impedance of the circuit is quite high at about 100kΩ, and it places little loading on the equipment from which the input signal is taken.

D4 prevents negative going input signals to the comparator from exceeding more than about 200mV or so. This is necessary because taking the inputs more negative than this can cause a parasitic transistor to be switched on. A parasitic transistor is one which is not a designed part of the i.c., but is nevertheless formed during the production of the i.c. If such a transistor was allowed to turn on it could easily cause a malfunction of the circuit.

Some readers may be surprised that the outputs of the comparators are connected in parallel. With most comparators and similar devices this would not be acceptable as it would result in a very large output current flowing when the paralleled outputs were at opposite states. This cannot occur here as the MC3302P has open collector outputs.

Construction

With the exceptions of D2 and D3, all the components are assembled on a 0.1in pitch stripboard panel which has 17 copper strips by 32 holes. The component layout and other details of this panel are shown in Fig. 12.2. Make sure that all 15 breaks in the copper strips and all 8 link wires are included. D4 and D4a are germanium diodes and it is advisable to use a heatshunt on each of their leadout wires as they are soldered into position. This greatly reduces the risk of these components being damaged by the heat from the soldering iron.

The circuit can be constructed as a self contained unit having its own case, battery supply, *on/off* switch and input sockets. In this event it should be connected to the main equipment via a twin screened lead. In many instances though, it will be more convenient to build the unit into the main equipment. Provided the input leads are fairly short they need not then be screened.

The circuit has a quiescent current consumption of approximately 3mA at 9V, but this increases by a maximum of about 10mA when both l.e.d. indicators come on. The unit can be powered from any supply voltage in the range 7.5 to about 18V or so.

Both l.e.d.s can be standard red types, but a more graphic display

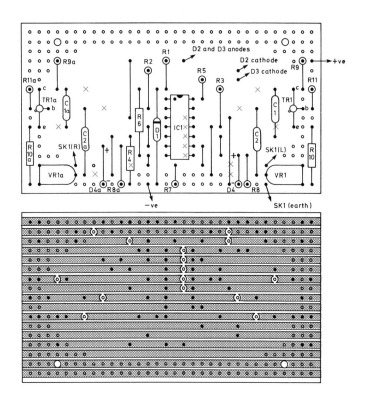

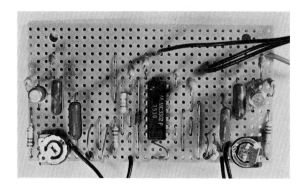

Figure 12.2

Stripboard layout for the complete indicator

66

will be obtained if D3 is a green or yellow type. If only a mono circuit is required the components marked with an 'a' suffix in Fig. 12.2 can be omitted, except for R8a. Resistors R3, R4, R6 and R7 should have tolerances of 2% or better, as otherwise it is likely that large errors will occur in the reference voltages with consequent poor accuracy between the two-l.e.d. switch on threshold levels.

Using the indicator

The way in which the correct settings for VR1 and VR1a are located will depend to some extent on the precise manner in which the unit is

Table 12.1. Components list for stereo peak level indicator

Resistors (all miniature ¼W, 5 or 10% except where noted)

R1	1.8kΩ
R2	820Ω
R3	24kΩ 2%
R4	12kΩ 2%
R5	820Ω
R6	47kΩ 2%
R7	47kΩ 2%
R8*	560kΩ
R9*	4.7kΩ
R10*	180Ω
R11*	1.8MΩ
VR1*	220kΩ sub-miniature horizontal preset

Capacitors

C1*	100nF type C280
C2*	100nF type C280

Semiconductors

TR1*	BC109
I.C.1	MC3302P
D1	BZY88C5V6 (5.6V, 400mW, zener)
D2	TIL209
D3	TIL209
D4*	OA91

Switch

S1	S.P.S.T. toggle or miniature toggle type

Miscellaneous
metal or plastics case
0.1 in matrix stripboard
panel holders for D2 and D3
input socket
PP6 battery and connector to suit
wire, solder, etc.

*Indicates that two of these components are required

to be used. Similarly, the best take off point for the input signal will depend on what type of equipment the circuit is to be used to monitor. A little common sense must be exercised here.

If, for example, the device is to be used to monitor the output of a stereo power amplifier, the inputs for the unit should obviously be obtained from the speaker outputs of the amplifier. The easiest way of finding the correct settings for the sensitivity controls is first to feed a signal into the amplifier and turn up the volume control to a level which clearly causes overloading. Then, with only one channel connected to the peak level indicator, adjust the appropriate preset for the lowest sensitivity which causes both l.e.d. indicators to come on. Finally, disconnect this input, connect the input for the other channel, and adjust the second preset sensitivity control in exactly the same way as the other one was adjusted.

It should not be too hard to devise similar setting up procedures if the unit is used in an application other than the one covered above.

13

Mono Amplifier

Needs 24V power.

This is a general purpose design which has two input sensitivities/ impedances. One input has a sensitivity of about 200mV r.m.s. for full output and its input impedance is 1MΩ. This is suitable for use with items of equipment such as crystal and ceramic pick-ups, tuners, and tape decks. The other input has a fairly high sensitivity and medium input impedance; the actual figures being about 20mV r.m.s. into 100kΩ for maximum output power. This is suitable for use with most guitar pickups and similar signal sources.

The maximum available output power is about 5W r.m.s. into an 8Ω loudspeaker. The output quality is not quite in the true hi-fi category, but it is very good with the total harmonic distortion level being typically no more than 1% at output powers of up to 5W r.m.s. The unit incorporates full bass and treble tone controls.

The circuit

The circuit schematic of the mono amplifier is given in Fig. 13.1. The power amplifier is based on I.C.1 which is a Texas Instruments SN76023N device. This is in some ways similar to an operational amplifier as it has both inverting (pin 16) and non-inverting (pin 1) inputs. However, unlike an operational amplifier it has a class B power amplifier output stage.

Half the power supply potential is available from an internal potential divider circuit at pin 2 of the device. This is used to bias the non-inverting input to virtually the same potential via R10 and R11. C10 decouples any noise or hum which is present on this bias voltage, and thus prevents it from being coupled to the non-inverting input. Virtually 100% negative feedback is provided over the amplifier at d.c. by R14. This gives the circuit a d.c. voltage gain of about unity, and so the output voltage is equal to the bias voltage fed to the non-inverting input. In this way the output voltage is set at the required level of half the supply voltage.

Some of the negative feedback via R14 is decoupled at audio frequencies by R12 and C11. The value of R12 determines the a.c. voltage gain of the circuit by controlling the amount of feedback which

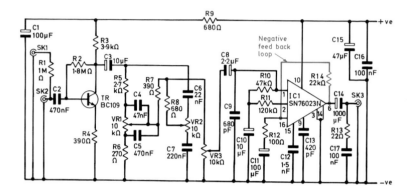

Figure 13.1

Mono amplifier circuit

is decoupled. C11 merely provides d.c. blocking. With the specified value for R12 and R14 the circuit has a voltage gain of about 220 times, as the circuit gain is roughly equal to R14 divided by R12.

C9, C12 and C13 are all needed to maintain the stability of the circuit. R13 and C17 are needed to compensate for the fact that the impedance of a loudspeaker greatly increases at high frequencies. This could otherwise lead to instability. These two components also help to prevent the circuit from becoming unstable when no loudspeaker is connected. Input d.c. blocking is provided by C8, and C14 provides the same function at the output. Supply decoupling is provided by C15 and C16.

The tone controls use a conventional passive circuit which is added ahead of the power amplifier. VR1 is the bass control and VR2 is the treble control. These provide more than 12dB of boost and cut at 100Hz and 10kHz when they are in their extreme settings. R7 and R8 are needed to minimise interaction between the two tone control circuits. VR3 is the volume control, and this is interposed between the tone control and power amplifier stages.

The input impedance to the tone controls is fairly low, and the input sensitivity here is too low for many applications as there is a considerable loss of signal through the tone control stages. A single transistor preamplifier stage is therefore used at the input in order to produce the required input sensitivities and impedances.

TR1 is used as the preamplifier, and it is connected in the common emitter configuration. The full voltage gain of TR1 is not needed, even on low level inputs, and so an unbypassed emitter resistor (R4) is used to provide negative feedback which reduces the voltage gain to approximately 10 times. It also greatly boosts the input impedance of the circuit. R3 is the collector load resistor for TR1 and base biasing is provided by R2. C2 blocks d.c. signals from TR1 base and C3 is the output d.c. blocking capacitor. High level signals do not require anything like the full gain of TR1 even after feedback has been applied, and so the high level input socket SK1 is coupled to the preamplifier input by way of attenuator resistor R1. This has the beneficial effect of greatly boosting the input impedance of the circuit so that it can be used satisfactorily with crystal and ceramic pickups. R9 and C1 are used to decouple the preamplifier supply rail.

Construction

Most of the components are assembled on a stripboard which has 24 copper strips by 46 holes, but it is more convenient to mount C4, C5, R7 and R8 on the tone control potentiometers. Details of the component panel and other wiring of the amplifier are all shown in Fig. 13.2.

Make quite certain that none of the 13 breaks in the copper strips is omitted, and that the two link wires are included. In fact great care must be taken to ensure that there are no errors as this could easily result in I.C.1 being destroyed. In particular, check for short circuits between copper strips caused by excess solder, especially in the vicinity of the i.c. Make absolutely sure that there is no short circuit between the copper strip which connects to the negative end of C14 and the strip which carries the negative supply rail. The SN76023N does not have output short circuit protection circuitry, and so any short circuit on the output could easily destroy the chip.

The SN76023N i.c. has a finned aluminium heatsink, and no further heatsinking is required by the device. This heatsink connects to the negative supply rail and so no component leads must be allowed to short circuit to it. Note that there is another version of the SN76023N i.c.; the SN76023ND, which does not have the heatsink and is therefore unsuitable for use in this design.

Provided the wiring between the controls and the component panel is reasonably short it is not necessary to use screened leads here. However, the leads which connect the component panel to the input sockets must be screened or there will be a strong pick up of mains hum and other interference.

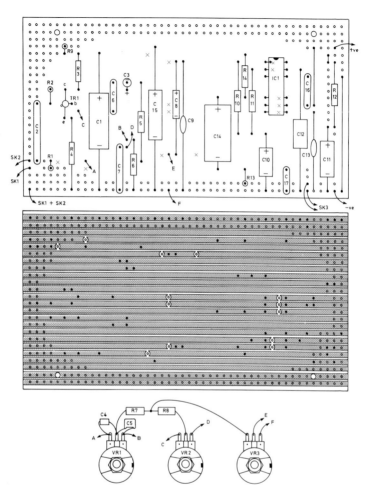

Figure 13.2

Component layout and potentiometer wiring

Table 13.1. Components list for mono amplifier

Resistors (all miniature, ¼W, 5 or 10%)

R1	1MΩ
R2	1.8MΩ
R3	3.9kΩ
R4	390Ω
R5	2.7kΩ
R6	270Ω
R7	390Ω
R8	680Ω
R9	680Ω
R10	47kΩ
R11	120kΩ
R12	100Ω
R13	22Ω
R14	22kΩ
VR1	10kΩ lin. carbon
VR2	10kΩ lin. carbon
VR3	10kΩ log. carbon

Capacitors

C1	100μF, 40V
C2	470nF type C280
C3	10μF, 25V
C4	47nF type C280
C5	470nF type C280
C6	22nF type C280
C7	220nF type C280
C8	2.2μF, 25V
C9	680pF ceramic plate
C10	10μF, 25V
C11	100μF, 16V
C12	1.5nF polystyrene, etc.
C13	470pF ceramic plate
C14	1,000μF, 16V
C15	47μF, 40V
C16	100nF type C280
C17	100nF type C280

Semiconductors

TR1	BC109
I.C.1	SN76023N

Miscellaneous
Case
0.1in matrix stripboard panel
three control knobs
input and output sockets
wire, solder, etc.

The unit can conveniently be built into a large cabinet which will house the amplifier, loudspeaker and power supply. A supply potential of about 24V is required, and the supply should not exceed 28V which is the absolute maximum rating of the SN76023N. The quiescent current consumption is only about 10mA, but this rises to something in the region of 500mA at high volume levels. It is not really practicable to use batteries to supply this sort of power, and a mains power supply, such as the one described at the end of this book, is required. Do not mount the power supply (particularly the mains transformer) close to the amplifier board and controls, as this could induce a high level of mains hum into the circuitry. If the controls are mounted on a metal panel this must be earthed to the negative supply rail. It is recommended that a loudspeaker having an impedance of other than 8Ω should not be used with this amplifier. Lower speaker impedances will be less efficient with regard to power consumption and will cause a slight reduction in the maximum output power. Higher speaker impedances will greatly reduce the available output power, which will only be about 3W into a 15Ω load, for instance.

Using the amplifier

The desired input is selected simply by connecting the input source to the appropriate input socket. Do not connect equipment to the low level input if full volume can be obtained with it connected to the high level input. To do so would result in increased distortion. Both inputs are very sensitive to pick up of mains hum and so screened leads must be used to connect the amplifier to other items of equipment. Do not leave unused ancillary equipment connected to one input when the other input is in use.

14

Simple Stereo Amplifier

Even using modern circuitry and components, a sophisticated stereo amplifier is a quite complex piece of equipment which falls outside the scope of this book. However, a simple but effective stereo amplifier can be produced using very simple circuitry these days, and such an amplifier is described below.

This design has the unusual and perhaps unique feature of using just one active device: a dual audio power amplifier i.c. The maximum output power is rather modest by modern standards at 2.5W r.m.s. per channel, but provided the unit is used in conjunction with fairly efficient loudspeakers, this will produce more than sufficient volume for most rooms. The output quality is very good with the level of total harmonic distortion being typically less than 0.1% at most power levels below 2W r.m.s. Due to crossover distortion, distortion does rise above this figure at very low output powers, but the actual percentage is still very low.

The unit has been designed primarily for use as a record player amplifier for use with a crystal or ceramic pickup. The input impedance and sensitivity (about 500kΩ and 300mV r.m.s. for full output respectively) also make the unit suitable for use with virtually any tape deck or radio tuner. It can, of course, be used with a magnetic pick-up or other low level signal source if a suitable preamplifier is added.

The circuit

Fig. 14.1 shows the circuit diagram for one channel of the amplifier. The two channels are basically identical.

The circuit is based on the National Semiconductors LM377N integrated circuit. The biasing of the unit is much the same as for the mono amplifier described in the previous section, with the non-inverting input of each amplifier being biased to about half the supply rail voltage

75

from an internal potential divider. The output of this divider circuit is available at pin 1 of the device, and it biases the non-inverting input of the amplifier via R1. This divider is used to bias both channels of the amplifier with C10 being used to ensure good isolation between channels and to provide supply decoupling.

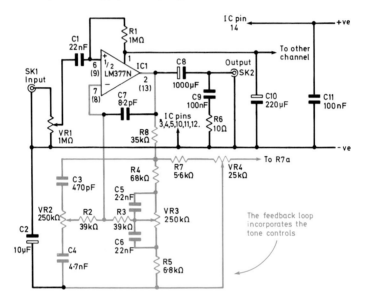

Figure 14.1

Circuit diagram of one channel of the amplifier. The other channel is virtually identical

A resistance must be included between the output of the amplifier and the non-inverting input so that the circuit has unity voltage gain at d.c., and the output of the amplifier is biased to the same potential as the non-inverting input (i.e. half the supply rail potential). In this design the tone control networks are included in the feedback circuitry, and so this resistance is not formed by a single resistor. This path is through R8, R4, VR3 and R3.

The purpose of including the tone controls in the feedback circuitry is that in this way the tone controls do not reduce the sensitivity and input impedance of the amplifier (as they did in the mono amplifier design, for instance). In this way the need for a preamplifier stage is avoided. The tone controls are quite conventional in design with VR2 providing treble boost and cut, and VR3 giving bass boost and cut. The input of the tone controls is fed from the output of the amplifier, and the output of the tone controls connects to the inverting input of the amplifier. The earth line of the tone controls is connected to the negative supply rail by d.c. blocking capacitor C2. The latter is necessary as the d.c. biasing of the amplifier would otherwise be affected by the bass tone control network.

Compared with a conventional passive tone control circuit, an active circuit of this type operates in reverse. For example, if VR2 is adjusted to provide treble boost, this produces increased feedback at treble frequencies and thus reduces the gain of the circuit at these frequencies. This does not matter in practice of course, as by reversing the track connections to VR2 and VR3 so that the cut and boost positions are reversed, the controls operate in the conventional manner (i.e. fully anticlockwise equals full cut, fully clockwise gives maximum boost).

Like the tone controls, the balance control is also included in the feedback circuit so that it does not shunt the input of the amplifier. The tone controls are not fed direct from the output of the amplifier, but are connected via a potential divider circuit. R8 forms the upper section of the potential divider and R7 plus part of VR4 form the lower section. This circuit is needed in order to reduce the amount of negative feedback which is applied to the amplifier as it would otherwise be excessive and this would give the amplifier an inadequate voltage gain. To some extent the amount by which the feedback is reduced is controlled by VR4. With VR4 slider at the centre of its track the amount of feedback which is eliminated is equal in both channels. However, adjusting VR4 off centre results in the gain of one amplifier being boosted and the gain of the other channel being reduced. Which channel is boosted and which is attenuated depends upon which way VR4 is adjusted. In this way the channels can be balanced. This system is slightly different to the conventional type of balance control, but it is just as effective and is by no means unique to this design.

Normally the LM377N requires no discrete stabilisation components, but the use of tone controls in the feedback circuit tends to encourage instability. Stabilisation is therefore provided by C7, C9 and R6.

VR1 is the volume control and input d.c. blocking is provided by C1. C11 is a supply decoupling component and this is common to both channels. C8 is the output coupling capacitor.

Construction

Most of the components are assembled on a 0.1in pitch stripboard panel which has 19 copper strips by 37 holes. Some are wired up on the tone controls, and all this wiring is illustrated in Fig. 14.2, which also gives details of the component panel. The tone control wiring for only one channel is shown as the two channels are identical. The two C9s and the two R6s are wired across the loudspeaker sockets. Most

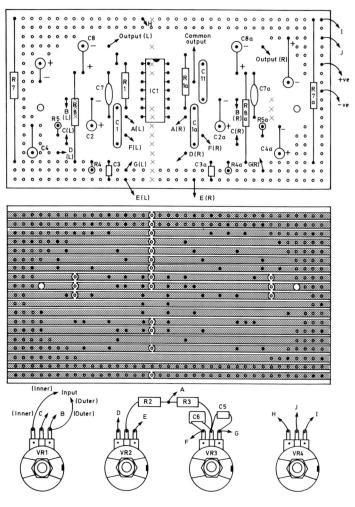

Figure 14.2

Component layout and wiring for the complete amplifier

of this wiring is quite straightforward, but screened leads must be used to connect the amplifier inputs to the volume control. The leads connecting the tone and balance controls to the component panel should be reasonably short, no more than 75 to 100mm (3—4 in) long.

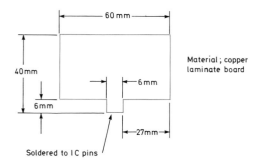

Figure 14.3

Details of the heat fins for the amplifier. Two of these fins are required

The LM377N does not have a built-on heatsink, and so suitable heatsinking must be provided. Suitable heatsinks can be constructed from copper laminate board (the board printed circuits are made from) cut to the shape shown in Fig. 14.3. Two of these are required, one being soldered to pins 3, 4 and 5 of the i.c., and the other being connected to pins 10, 11 and 12. These heatsinks can be clearly seen in the photograph of the prototype amplifier. The pins of the i.c. and the relevant part of each heatsink must be very generously tinned with solder before soldering the heatfins into position. Make each soldered connection quite quickly so that there is no danger of the i.c. being overheated and damaged. Also, make sure that excess solder does not connect to pins of the i.c. other than the intended ones. Remember that the heatfins are connected to the negative supply rail, and short circuits could occur if component leads are allowed to come into electrical contact with them.

Both thermal shutdown and output short circuit protection circuitry are built into the LM377N i.c., and so it will not be damaged by being overdriven or short circuits on the output. The heatfins described here should be adequate for normal usage, but they can be increased in size if the amplifier is likely to be driven at full output for prolonged periods. The amplifier may not perform satisfactorily if the size of the heatfins is reduced or if they are simply omitted altogether.

The unit requires a power supply potential of about 20V (26V absolute maximum). The supply voltage should not be very much less than 20V as this would reduce the maximum output power. The quiescent current

Table 14.1. Components list for the simple stereo amplifier

Resistors (all miniature ¼W, 5%)
R1*	1MΩ
R2*	39kΩ
R3*	39kΩ
R4*	68kΩ
R5*	6.8kΩ
R6*	10Ω
R7*	5.6kΩ
R8*	33kΩ
VR1	1MΩ dual gang carbon log.
VR2	250kΩ (or 220kΩ) dual gang carbon lin.
VR3	250kΩ (or 220kΩ) dual gang carbon lin.
VR4	25kΩ (or 22kΩ) carbon lin.

Capacitors
C1*	22nF type C280
C2*	10µV, 16V
C3*	470pF polystyrene
C4*	4.7nF polystyrene
C5*	2.2nF polystyrene
C6*	22nF type C280
C7*	8.2pF ceramic
C8*	1,000µF, 10V
C9*	100nF type C280
C10	220µF, 16V
C11	100nF type C280

Semiconductor
I.C.1	LM377N

Miscellaneous
case
0.1in matrix stripboard panel
input and output sockets
heat tabs (see text)
wire, solder, etc.

*indicates that two of these components are required.

consumption is only about 15mA, but this rises to several hundred milliamperes at high volume levels. Battery operation is therefore not very practicable, and a main power supply such as the one described next in this book is really required. Do not mount the power supply components, especially the transformer and leads carrying the mains supply, close to the amplifier circuitry.

The amplifier outputs connect to 8Ω speakers which should be capable of handling at least 2.5W r.m.s. and should be housed in proper cabinets. It is recommended that only 8Ω loudspeakers are used with this design.

Always use screened connecting leads at the input as there will otherwise probably be an excessive pick up of mains hum. For the same reason it is advisable for the component bodies of VR1 to VR4 to be earthed to the negative supply rail.

15

Stabilised Power Supply

This power supply is primarily intended for use with the slave amplifier, mono amplifier and simple stereo amplifier which are described in Projects 10, 13 and 14 in this book, although it is suitable as a power source for many other audio amplifier designs. It will provide a nominal output voltage of either 19 or 23V depending upon the operating voltage selected for the zener diode employed in the unit. A maximum output current of several hundred milliamperes is available. The output is well smoothed and a low output hum level is obtained from an amplifier which is powered from this unit.

The main reason for using a stabilised supply is that the difference in output voltage between low load and full output is quite high for an unstabilised supply. For example, a supply which gives 20V under full load may well provide some 30V or so under little or no load. Such a supply would be unsuitable for use with, say, the simple stereo amplifier design, as although it requires a supply voltage of 20V at maximum output, and would receive it, this design must not have a supply potential of more than 26 volts. This is the absolute maximum which the i.c. can withstand. Obviously an unstabilised supply would exceed this figure. The same sort of problem exists with the other two amplifiers mentioned above, and, in fact, with most other modern power amplifiers.

The potential difference between no load and full load of an unstabilised supply can be reduced by using a mains transformer having a secondary current rating which is well in excess of the maximum current drawn by the supplied equipment, but such a transformer would be relatively bulky and expensive. A better alternative is to use a simple regulator circuit to reduce the unloaded output voltage to a safe level. As the regulator circuit also provides electronic smoothing of the output, this also provides better performance with regard to output hum level.

82

The circuit

Fig. 15.1 shows the complete circuit diagram of the stabilised power supply unit. The mains supply is connected to the primary winding of T1 via *on/off* switch S1. LP1 is a panel neon which acts as the *on/off* indicator.

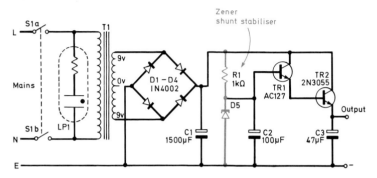

Figure 15.1

Stabilised p.s.u. circuit diagram

On the prototype, T1 is a 9V − 0V − 9V transformer which has the 0V tapping ignored. A transformer having an 18V secondary winding of the appropriate current rating would be equally suitable. The output from the secondary is fullwave rectified by the bridge rectifier formed by D1 to D4. The rough d.c. output from the rectifier is smoothed by C1.

The regulator circuit is a conventional emitter follower series type circuit. R1 and D5 form an ordinary zener shunt stabiliser circuit, and C2 smoothes out any noise or hum which is present across D5. The stabilised voltage produced by D5 is at quite a high impedance and cannot supply the fairly high current requirements of an audio power amplifier. Therefore an emitter follower stage is used as a buffer to provide a suitably low output impedance. Actually an emitter follower Darlington pair is used here as a high level of gain is needed in order to produce really good results.

There is some voltage drop between the base of TR1 and the output at the emitter of TR2, and a germanium transistor is used in the TR1 position rather than a silicon type in order to minimise this drop. The actual voltage drop is only something in the region of 1V. Thus a 20V zener in the D5 position will produce an output potential of approximately 19V, which is suitable for use with the simple stereo amplifier design. The slave and mono amplifiers require a slightly higher supply voltage and D5 should have an operating potential of

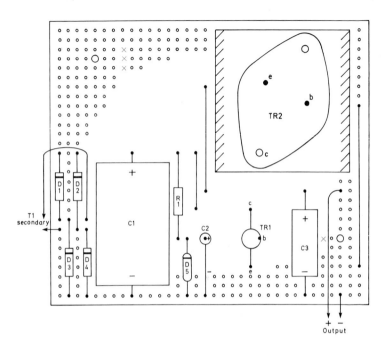

Figure 15.2   Component layout on the matrix board

24V if the supply is to be used with either of these designs. This produces an output potential of about 23V. D5 can be any type of zener which has a power rating of 400mW or more (the popular BZY88 series are perfectly suitable).

Final smoothing of the output is provided by C3.

Construction

Most of the components are accommodated on a 0.1in stripboard panel having 29 copper strips by 34 holes. Details of this component panel are given in Fig. 15.2. There are just four breaks in the copper strips.

TR2, although a power transistor, fits onto the component panel. It is fitted with a small vaned type heatsink (as shown in the photograph). TR2 is not only mounted by having its emitter and base pins soldered to the panel, but it is also held in place by two 4B.A. mounting bolts. The lower of these (as seen in Fig. 15.2) connects the collector of TR3 to the component panel. The metal casing of TR2 is its collector terminal incidentally.

TR1 is a germanium transistor and is therefore relatively easily damaged by heat. A heatshunt should be used on each of its leadout wires as they are soldered into position and it is advisable not to cut the leadout wires of this component very short.

The power supply will presumably be housed in the same case as the amplifier, although the two units should not be mounted too close together as this could result in hum being induced from the power supply wiring to the amplifier circuitry. For reasons of safety the case should be a type which does not permit easy access to exposed mains wiring. The negative supply rail should be connected to the mains earth lead and if a metal case is used this must also be earthed. In fact any exposed metal work should be earthed for reasons of safety. The mains plug should be fitted with a 3A fuse, and it is also a good idea to connect a 1A fuse between one side of T1 secondary and the appropriate input of the bridge rectifier.

LP1 must be a proper neon panel indicator having an integral series resistor for normal mains operation. Straightforward neon bulbs are not suitable.

Using the power supply unit

Before connecting the finished supply to an amplifier it is a good idea to check that the output voltage is at approximately the correct level. It is advisable to connect a resistor of a few kilohms in value across the output of the supply to act as a load for the output transistors when making this measurement. Otherwise it is quite possible that the current through these transistors will be so low that they will not function correctly, with misleading readings being obtained in consequence. Note that due to the tolerance of the zener diode and other factors, the

Table 15.1. Components list for the stabilised power supply

Resistor	
R1	1kΩ, ¼W, 5%
Capacitors	
C1	1500µF, 30V
C2	100µF, 25V
C3	47µF, 25V
Semiconductors	
TR1	AC127
TR2	2N3055
D1 to D4	1N4002 (4 off)
D5	see text
Transformer	
T1	Standard mains primary, 18V, 1A secondary (or 9—0—9V) with centre tap ignored
Switch	
S1	D.P.S.T. mains rotary or toggle type
Indicator	
LP1	Mains panel neon having integral series resistor
Miscellaneous	
0.1in matrix stripboard panel	
heatsink for TR2 (small finned type)	
mains lead, 2A fused mains plug, connecting wire, solder, etc.	

actual output voltage can easily be 1V or so different from the specified nominal figure.

If the output voltage is not correct, measure the voltage across D5 to see if it is equal to its marked zener voltage. If it is, then the fault is almost certainly in the output transistors. If it is not, check the wiring of T1 and the rectifier network. D5 must be connected with the correct polarity or the voltage developed across it will only be a fraction of a volt. Make quite sure that no mains wiring is accidentally touched when fault finding or testing the unit.

When all is well, connect the supply to the amplifier ensuring that the unit is connected with the correct polarity. If the polarity should accidentally be reversed it is quite likely that the amplifier and possibly even the power supply will sustain expensive damage.